When Christians Disagree
Series Editor: Oliver R. Barclay

Creation and Evolution
Editor: Derek Burke

Creation and Evolution

Edited by Derek Burke

E. H. Andrews
O. R. Barclay
R. J. Berry
D. C. Burke
A. G. Fraser
D. T. Gish
D. G. Jones
V. Wright

WHEN CHRISTIANS DISAGREE

Inter-Varsity Press

INTER-VARSITY PRESS
38 De Montfort Street, Leicester LE1 7GP

Chapters 2 and 8 are shortened versions of essays published
in *God, Science and Evolution*, © 1980 by Evangelical Press
and Services Ltd.

First published 1985

British Library Cataloguing in Publication Data

When Christians disagree
  1. Evolution—Religious aspects—Christianity
I. Burke, Derek
233'.11   BT712
ISBN 0-85110-720-6

Set in Linotron Sabon
Phototypeset in Great Britain by
Input Typesetting Ltd., London SW19 8DR
Printed in Great Britain at the University Press, Oxford

*Inter-Varsity Press is the publishing division of the
Universities and Colleges Christian Fellowship (formerly the
Inter-Varsity Fellowship), a student movement linking
Christian Unions in universities and colleges throughout the
United Kingdom and the Republic of Ireland, and a member
movement of the International Fellowship of Evangelical
Students. For information about local and national activities
write to UCCF, 38 De Montfort Street, Leicester LE1 7GP.*

When Christians Disagree

Introducing the series

There are many subjects on which the teaching of the Bible is quite clear. There is a substantial core of Christian theology and ethics that we can confidently proclaim as 'biblical teaching', and those rejecting as well as those accepting the authority of that teaching will agree that such a core exists.

As we try to work out the application of biblical teaching in detail, however, we find areas in which there is no such clear consensus. Christians who are trying equally to be obedient to the teaching of Christ and his carefully instructed apostles come to different conclusions about such subjects as baptism and church government. Some of their differences have been resolved after debate. In Protestant circles, for instance, few would now wish, as some once did, to excommunicate people for advocating birth control. Further discussion has brought substantial agreement. Some questions, however, are not so easily resolved at present; and there is a need for healthy discussion among Christians so that we may arrive, if possible, at an agreed view. If that is not possible, then all of us need to re-examine our view in the light of Scripture and to exchange views, so that we may ensure that our position is not the product of wishful thinking, but is really faithful to the Bible. All of us are influenced in our thinking by our traditions, our education and the general climate of thought of our age. These forces tend to mould our ideas more than we realize, and to make us conform to the fashion of our time, or the traditions in which we were brought up, rather than to revealed truth.

This series of books under the title of *When Christians Disagree* attempts to tackle some of these current debates. Each book has the same fundamental structure. A series of starting 'theses', or a statement of a position (usually excluding the more extreme views on either side), has been sent to the writers. They have been asked to agree or disagree with the 'theses' and to set out a Christian position as they see it. They then have the opportunity to respond to one or more of the other articles written from a different point of view from their own. A short closing summary attempts to clarify the main issues in debate.

All the contributors seek to be ruled by Scripture. Since they do not agree between themselves, the crucial issue is whether one view or another is more consistent with the teaching of the Bible. Some of the problems arise out of the impact upon us of new cultural patterns. These new patterns may or may not be healthy, and that has to be judged by the application of biblical truth which is always health-giving – the good and acceptable and perfect will of God. We are not arguing whether it is easier to believe or do one thing or another in today's world. We are not even asking whether a Christian position seems stupid to the cultured man of today. We are asking whether there are revealed principles that give us at least some guidelines, and perhaps even a clear answer to our problems.

The Bible is authoritative in more than one way: in some areas explicit teaching is given; in other areas the question is left open in such a way that we know there is no universal 'right' answer. Worship provides an example. There are some broad principles; but the Bible seems authoritatively to allow, and perhaps implicitly to encourage, variety in the details of the style and ordering of worship. In such cases we will solve the problem in our own age and culture in obedience to the more basic explicit teachings that we have.

In the areas that this series explores there are some things laid down clearly in Scripture and some that are not. There is, for instance, no biblical instruction as to whether husband or wife should dig the garden; there are no explicit limits drawn to the coercive powers of the state, nor any delineation of the nature of the world before the fall – except that it was very good.

The arguments, therefore, concern first of all whether the Bible does or does not settle certain questions and, secondly, how far we can go in confident application of those biblical truths that we are given. The demarcation line between these here is important. If we can agree what is clearly taught, then all else is in a secondary category, where we know that human opinion is fallible. Some of our discussion is above the line and is therefore most important. Some falls below it and cannot be as vital, even if in pratical terms we have to adopt a policy.

OLIVER R. BARCLAY

Contents

9

Contents

An introduction to this book

D. C. Burke

One subject over which Christians disagree is evolution.

The debate over the implications of evolution for the Christian faith began over 100 years ago. Precipitated by the publication of Darwin's *On the Origin of Species* in 1859 and brought to wide public notice by a debate at the British Association in 1860, the question at issue was twofold: Was the world created over a short period of time some 6,000 years ago, or not? and, Was man related to and derived from the higher apes? If the latter was so, what happened to the biblical statement that man was created 'in the image of God' – was it still valid? Both Christians and their opponents had much at stake – the Christians felt threatened by what were undoubtedly attempts to rid the world of religious explanations once and for all, and they reacted strongly – some would say over-reacted.

A century and a quarter later the debate still continues. A series of books, mainly from the USA, putting forcefully a case for a seven-day creation and against the theory of evolution has persuaded many Christians that they have to choose between the traditional interpretation of Genesis 1 and the findings of modern science. Such choices create problems – for Christians who feel that either they must reject the biology they learnt in school or university, or at least not think about it, and for scientists who broadly accept the theory of evolution and who then feel that they have no place in the evangelical church.

How far apart are the two sides? There are certainly Christians who differ radically in their attitude to the theory of evolution; do they have anything in common, and what are the issues that separate them? It is the aim of this book to define these. The area of common ground was defined in the following set of theses which were taken as common ground, and which conclude by stating the nub of the debate: 'This debate is about whether such large-scale changes have taken place over a period greater than 6,000 years, and whether Genesis 1 excludes or allows that possibility.'

A word about how the book came to be written. Initially, six people (Professor Andrews and Dr Fraser, Dr Gish and Professor Jones, Professors Berry and Wright) were sent the theses and asked to write chapters on subjects on which they were expert. The chapters were grouped in pairs, so that two differing views – one broadly supporting and the other opposing the theory of evolution – could be set side by side. Each author was then given the opportunity to comment briefly on the other author's work. Professor Andrews saw Dr Fraser's chapter before he wrote his own, and also suggested that he should write a chapter on the philosophical aspects of the debate – which then paired well with Professor Jones's chapter. That, however, left a need for a chapter to pair with Dr Gish's, and this I wrote – after seeing the other contribution but giving Dr Gish the opportunity to reply to it. Since I was a contributor, I did not attempt to summarize the debate myself, but asked Dr Oliver Barclay to review the whole and provide a conclusion, which itself was read in draft and commented on by Professor Andrews and myself.

In this way I think readers will agree that justice has been done.

Opening theses

1. In the beginning God created the heavens and the earth (Gn. 1:1). God's creation is a sovereign act of his power, love and wisdom and depends on no other being or already-created substance. It was *ex nihilo*.

2. Whatever their beliefs about God's methods in the creation, no Christian relying on the Scriptures extrapolates from the material universe to the moral world of men. The end of each phase of creation is that 'God saw that it was good'. The judgment of the Scriptures on men's behaviour is that it stands deserving not of the approval, but of the judgment, of God. The Christian therefore stands opposed to theories of 'evolutionary ethics', 'evolutionary politics', 'evolutionary philosophy', *etc*. No scientific theory of creation can be more than a discussion of God's *possible* methods.

3. If God chose to use processes to complete his creation, it was still his sovereign act. We cannot say that God's sovereign acts are always sudden and without processes. The events of nature represent God's sovereignty, whether they are subject to scientific explanation or not. There is no reason in principle to think of a sudden creative act as more God-like than a process.

4. The interpretation of Genesis 1 is crucial to differing Christian views. This chapter is internally consistent in its own right, but the reader must decide into what category the narrative falls – history (what kind?), poetry, science, or symbolism, *etc*. Other scriptures and the evidence of the senses need to be taken into account here, just as they do in the interpretation of any other passage; *i.e.* mention of the four corners of the earth, or the hills clapping their hands.

5. The New Testament regards Adam and Eve as the first parents of the whole human race (*Homo sapiens*). They were presumably not the ancestors of other hominoids. Their dates cannot be fixed from the biblical data, since the genealogies are apparently not complete.

6. Death must have been present in the plant and animal kingdom before the fall, since, for example, no animal could eat grass or go for a walk without killing many small animals and plants. The presence of death in the plant and animal kingdom may have increased since the fall, but we must not regard the death of large numbers of organisms as in itself evil.

7. Such animal and plant death might have led to the extinction of species, but if so, we must attribute that to God's sovereign wisdom, and not to evil forces. The small-scale changes in existing animal and plant species which we can observe, or which we can bring about by artificial selection, must also be seen to be included in God's wisdom and sovereignty. We cannot therefore argue against evolution from the moral nature of these processes.

8. While we cannot be certain of the exact scientific or historical status of the animal and plant kinds described in Genesis 1, the biblical account enables us to appreciate the creation and fall in concrete terms. No alternative ways of talking about them provide an adequate substitute. The biblical account cannot therefore be superseded, though it may be supplemented, by a scientific account.

9. The extension from observable processes to general biological principles, a part of the inductive method of the natural sciences, is not logically watertight, but can usually be tested by the process of falsification. This is not possible for the theory of evolution by natural selection, because it is locked in historical time, but that does not necessarily invalidate the theory as a correct explanation of what has been observed. Any alternative explanation must explain the considerable body of accumulated data equally well.

10. Scientific evidence gives the world a very great age. This could be a consequence of great antiquity, or of the relatively recent creation of the world as a going concern. It would in the latter case have an apparent age which did not correspond to the actual age: some newly-created sedimentary rocks would appear to be millions of years old; newly-created trees might have 1,000 rings and seem to be 1,000 years old, and Adam might seem to be about twenty years old on his first day. Then the scientist would be correct in scientific terms to detect an age and a process which had not in fact taken place. He could not be expected to detect the sudden creation. If we assert a creation of six 24-hour days in the recent past, it will therefore be on biblical and not scientific grounds. The scientific findings must be expected to appear to contradict it to some extent.

11. It is possible to establish the fact that species can and do change on a very small scale. Everyone is agreed that this is so. If all the races of men are of common origin, then changes have taken place which could properly be called 'evolutionary'. What can actually be proved, however, is only very small-scale, and for the purposes of this debate it may be better to exclude the word 'evolution' from such changes and use it only for large-scale changes. Thus, this debate is about whether such large-scale changes have taken place over a period greater than 6,000 years, and whether Genesis 1 excludes or allows that possibility.

1
The age of the earth

A. G. Fraser

The age of the earth deduced from its history · Evidence from rocks · Evidence from fossils · Evidence from radiometric dating · Orthodox geology and other views · Flood geology · The 'apparent age' view · Final comments and conclusions

What is the basis of orthodox geological reasoning? How do geologists establish time-scales for the earth? In this paper, I should like to explain why geologists believe the age of the earth to be as they suppose, and how this belief relates to organic evolution. Then I should like to analyse alternative models of an earth only 10,000 years old, created in six literal days. Finally, I wish to propose some principles of biblical interpretation which we need to consider.

The age of the earth deduced from its history: discovering the past by reference to the present

Evidence from rocks
The features of any rock depend on three things: the nature of the source material, the environment under which it was formed, and the influence upon it of subsequent geological events.

I shall concentrate here on sedimentary rocks; that is, rocks formed from the breakdown of pre-existing rocks. Sedimentary rocks comprise about 80% of the rocks exposed at the earth's surface, and reflect clearly the influence of the three factors above. Their study has been crucial in obtaining information about the history and age of the earth.

The importance of the environment under which sediments were deposited is paramount. We may investigate the *kind of land surface* (mountainous or plain); the *regime of sedimentation* (river, lake, delta, estuary, swamp, lagoon, shelf sea, ocean basin or desert); the *agency of deposition* (wind, water, ice, organic or chemical precipitation); and the *climate*. By examining all these aspects, the geologist can draw a detailed picture of the geographical conditions prevailing when the sediments were formed. From the mineral or organic content, and from a wide variety of other features, specific factors in the environment can be identified. These include depth of water, the strength and direction of water or wind currents, and whether the sediment accumulated continuously or intermittently, rapidly or slowly. Depending on the size of the rock fragments or mineral grains in the sediment, the nature of the source rock can be determined by inspection either at its location or in the laboratory. Frequently the source rock itself can be identified, so that the distance travelled by the sediment particles can also be estimated.

But how can such detailed deductions be made when a rock is the product of processes which no-one has actually observed? Here we come to a fundamental point in the current debate among Christians concerning earth models. The geologist (rightly, I believe) operates by analogy with the present. He uses contemporary analogues of slowly or rapidly forming sediments to make reasoned conclusions about the ancient environment. In most cases he can make an excellent correlation.

This approach does not mean that geologists believe that all processes acted slowly and uniformly with time. The 'uniformitarianism' I have been describing assumes only the constancy of physical laws underlying geological processes, but accepts that the processes themselves may occur at very different rates. Catastrophic events may thus be allowed for in the theory.

I should like to move from theory to two practical examples of geological analysis from my personal knowledge. In the far north-west of Scotland and the Hebrides, there are distinctive red sedimentary rocks called the Torridonian sediments. These sediments have a thickness of more than 4 kilometres in some areas, as much as 8 kilometres on the island of Rhum. They display a great variety of structures, most of them closely similar to those in deposits of mountainous semi-desert regions of today. A modern environment of this kind is characterized by strong erosion of the mountainous tract, swift removal of eroded material during occasional violent storms, the build-up of fans or cones of sediment where the rivers discharge much of their loads, and the spreading outward and overlapping of these fans to form a river flood-plain which in time reaches a lake or the sea.

These environmental characteristics are clearly stamped on the Torridonian sediments. River channels are marked by trough-shaped structures filled with rocky fragments becoming progressively smaller from the base upwards, reflecting the way the river deposited its load. The channels occur at many different levels in the Torridonian succession, showing the great persistence of these conditions. Numerous, separate and extensive layers of sediment more uniform in thickness and particle size represent, by analogy, deposits laid down by vast sheets of water spilling over river banks in times of flood. The fact that the flooding was intermittent is proved by the presence, in the river-borne material, of pebbles which had time to be shaped by wind-blown sand. Strong oxidation of iron-bearing minerals, well known in modern deserts, has given the characterisitc red colour.

Ripples in the sediments show that the current of the Torridonian rivers flowed mainly from north-west to south-east, a conclusion confirmed by increases in the rock fragment size towards that direction. Other clues indicate that the Torridonian mountains must once have occupied an area now covered by the North Atlantic ocean. As the sediments are traced to the south-east, they change progressively into different rocks whose lithology and internal features indicate deposition under the sea. In places, actual shorelines can be observed, with spectacular examples of sea cliffs and beach deposits.

Mark the chronological implications of this description.

Reasoning strictly from the observed rate of sedimentation in modern semi-desert areas of high relief, it is clear that the Torridonian succession must represent many thousands, if not millions, of years in view of its tremendous thickness. And it must be remembered that these sediments represent only a fraction of geological time in that location. Also, the geologist can discriminate between geological processes occurring on very different time-scales, distinguishing between the metre or more of sediment which could have been laid down by a single flood, and the smoothing and shaping of pebbles by wind-borne sand, which must have taken a vastly longer time.

The second example I wish to mention relates to the widely occurring sandstones, shales (sediments consisting mostly of clay) and local thin coals of the Pennines in northern England. The structures, relationships and proportions of the sediments are all remarkably consistent with those of a modern delta, such as the Niger or the Mississippi. Recent research has produced an extraordinarily detailed picture of the environmental framework which must have existed when these particular Pennine sediments were deposited. The correlation with extant deltas is based on a whole set of observational data, not on isolated features. Known geological causes are easily sufficient to account for the scale of the delta complex: the delta of the Brahmaputra and Ganges rivers in Bangladesh is larger than the whole of the British Isles.

These two examples illustrate the principles by which ancient geographical settings (known as palaeogeographies) are established. By a simple extension of these principles, the geologist determines such information as the land and sea distribution for any particular geological period, the topography of the land, the location of rivers, deltas and lakes, the direction of moving water, and the depth, temperature and salinity of the sea.

Reconstructing the geography of an ancient period in earth history in the way we have described often brings to light some fascinating features. Consider, for instance, the reassembly of the Devonian period some 400 million years ago. In this geological period, two categories of sediments are distinguished; one of continental origin (rocks laid down on the land surface by rivers, or found in deltas at the margins of inland lakes), and the other marine (laid down under the sea). When North America and Europe are fitted together in what seems to have been their former relative positions, one can follow through the Devonian shoreline, and several remarkable facts then become apparent. Richly oil-bearing Devonian sediments in Russia and in Canada bear an almost identical relationship to the Devonian continent; both regions have previously constituted offshore reefs.

Furthermore, huge deposits of evaporites (potash, salt, *etc.*) occur in Devonian sediments in geographical settings which were closely comparable in that period, but not now. They are found in close proximity to the Devonian shoreline, where one would expect basins of salt water to be cut off periodically, subsequently evaporating to give precipitated salt deposits, just as happens today in the Persian Gulf.

Palaeogeographic reconstructions are rather analogous to the assembly of a jigsaw puzzle. Once the general picture begins to take shape, reasoned predictions can be made on the nature and location of pieces of evidence not hitherto found. Modern methods in geology provide many examples of projected reconstructions confirmed, some with considerable economic consequences. One can cite in this connection the discovery of the concealed coalfields of Kent and the South Midlands in England. Similarly, palaeogeographic reconstructions have successfully predicted both the nature and distribution of metalliferous deposits in the Antarctic continent. Again, the location of oil in the thick sedimentary succession under the North Sea highlights the close relationship between specific rock types and their economic potential on the one hand, and the environments in which they originated on the other. Any proposed geological model radically different from the one supported here must be able to make such predictions equally well or better.

Orthodox geological analysis not only permits the detailed characterization of ancient geographies, but also enables a sequence of *changing* geographical patterns to be discovered. This is well illustrated in the area of north-west Scotland already discussed. The red Torridonian sediments are overlain by pale-coloured, sandy sediments indicating that their desert conditions had changed. In lithology and internal structure, these lighter sediments can be matched with sediments being deposited now at the margins of the North Sea; therefore, deposition at some time on a shallow marine shelf is inferred. Apparently there was a long time-gap between the old and new conditions, since, judging by great variations in the thickness of the Torridonian rocks over short distances, the Torridonian sediment was extensively stripped away first. In turn, the light-coloured sandy sediments give way upwards to chemically precipitated limestones, proving that marine conditions continued, but with deeper water and an increase in dissolved carbon dioxide.

Determining this sequence of environmental changes depends on the Law of Superposition, which states that rocks resting on top of others are usually younger than the ones below. The general truth of this law can be demonstrated from the example above, because the bottom layers of sediment overlying the Torridonian contain abundant fragments of the latter within them. But the normal order can be reversed by geological events subsequent to the formation of the sediments. The area we are considering is a case in point. For when these different types of sediment – red Torridonian desert sandstones, pale sandstones, and limestones, – in that order upwards, are traced east, this sequence is commonly reversed, and the Torridonian rocks themselves may be topped by the very rocks on which, farther west, they themselves are sitting.

This kind of reversal is characteristic of mountain belts all over the world, and is the result of major upheavals in the earth's crust which affected much of the British Isles around this time, especially the north of Scotland. Another far-reaching change in the environment was obviously introduced by this event, so that an area once occupied by a relatively shallow sea in which sands and limestones were deposited was replaced by a large mountain range, believed to have once rivalled the Alps.

Before going on, we need to look at two important

ramifications of these ideas, since they bear directly on some of the current controversies. First, although the upside-down nature of the sediments was readily recognizable in the case cited, it can also be proved in other ways. For example, the ripple structures in the sandstones are the wrong way up where the rocks are inverted. Other internal criteria can be used equally well. Consequently, a wrong order in sediments can generally be identified even where the correct sequence may not be known, though it usually is. One criterion which is sometimes used is a reversed order of fossils, but in fact the geologist is rarely, if ever, solely dependent on this. Thus, a situation where older fossils lie above younger ones is not the problem it may at first appear.

Second, mountain-forming introduces us to the possibility of catastrophe somewhat different in kind from any we have already considered. It is highly probable that mountains resulted from a catastrophic process – in the sense that the rate of geological activity was greatly increased, and/or that known forces were more potent than usual. Nevertheless, and this is an important point, their construction must have taken an appreciable time to accomplish. From what we know about the physical and mechanical properties of rocks, the folding and bending of strata in mountain belts could have resulted only from forces acting slowly over a considerable period, because rapidly acting forces would cause rocks to break rather than to bend. Breaks of this type, called 'faults' or 'thrusts', are themselves present in mountain areas, showing yet again that the geologist can recognize processes involving substantially different rates of time.

We compared the mountain range crossing northern Scotland at the time of its formation with the present-day Alps. One reason (out of many) for so doing is that flanking the margins of the Scottish Highlands are deposits of rubbly material of great thickness, up to 7 kilometres, closely comparable to sediments which have accumulated at the edge of the Alps and other mountain ranges. These deposits are erosional products originating in the mountainous area: one can readily identify, in the fragments, rock types present in the mountains themselves. The Scottish Highlands of today are therefore merely the eroded stumps of a major mountain chain which extended into Scandinavia, Greenland and north-east America. By analogy with present rates of erosion in the Alps and Himalayas, one must infer a time interval of the order of hundreds of millions of years. The magnitude of this interval is fully consistent with the succeeding periods of sedimentation and the environmental changes they signify which are documented in the general geological record of the British Isles.

The method by which the sequence of changing geographies was traced in north-west Scotland is applicable in any other geographical area. And so, by relating the geological histories of widely separated parts, environmental variations on a world-wide scale can be deciphered. The geological history of Great Britain is typical: a pattern of continual and profound changes in the land and sea distribution, of ever-changing topography, of recurring cycles of erosion, deposition and crustal upheaval, of fluctuations in climate, and so on. These changes did not, however, proceed at a uniform rate. Rather, long periods in which environmental conditions persisted essentially unchanged, or varied only very slowly, were interrupted by relatively shorter periods of dramatic, indeed catastrophic, change. Similar conclusions are reached from all other regions of the world.

It is impossible here to follow all the lines of evidence of the earth's age which exist in sedimentary rocks, but before leaving this section, I should like to look briefly at other sorts of rocks which add their own testimony to the length and complexity of the earth's history. Rocks which have crystallized from a molten state (*magma*) are described as igneous rocks. They are termed *volcanic* if they have cooled rapidly at or near the earth's surface, and *plutonic* if they have cooled slowly deep within the earth's crust. The products of volcanic activity include not only the familiar lava flows at the surface, but also sheets formed by the freezing of magma as it cuts its way through the rocks underneath the volcano. Sedimentary rocks pierced by the ascending magma are not usually greatly altered by the heat, since its effect is relatively short-lived.

With plutonic rocks, however, where the magma rose up into overlying sediments, but failed to approach the surface and crystallized slowly at depth, the heating effects are usually much greater. The sediments are transformed, and are said to be *metamorphosed*. The internal fabric of the sediment is replaced and new minerals develop, the nature of which depends on the original sediment and on the temperatures and pressures of the metamorphic episode.

Many examples of this phenomenon could be given from all parts of the world. Two from Britain which I know very well are the Skiddaw Granite in the Lake District, and the Comrie 'Granite' in Perthshire, Scotland. In both cases, the heating effect of the plutonic rock extends outwards for at least 0.5 kilometre from its margin and, as expected, the changes in the surrounding sediments increase progressively as the contact is approached. Thus, the rocks least affected are vaguely spotted with new minerals just beginning to form, whereas nearer to the plutonic rock the sediments have completely recrystallized and have a totally new set of minerals. These same minerals can also be made in the laboratory, and the measured temperatures and pressures at which they form can be used to decide how hot the sediments were during the metamorphism. Furthermore, from known factors such as the heat conductivity of rocks, the latent heat of crystallization in magma, and so on, it is possible to determine theoretically the time required to raise by a specific amount the temperature of a sedimentary rock into which magma has been emplaced. For large granites, it has been calculated that more than one million years are needed to heat the sediment to a temperature consistent with the new minerals produced in it.

Whether igneous rocks are volcanic or plutonic, they allow the geological time-table to be filled in more completely, since one can readily distinguish whether the deposition of sediments occurred before or after periods of igneous activity. Igneous rocks and associated metamorphic phenomena crop up repeatedly throughout geological time. They occur characteristically in mountain belts, allowing still more detailed analysis of the series of events involved in mountain building. Their abundance in mountain belts suggests that the 'catastrophic' episodes which punctuate the otherwise slow environmental transitions in the geological record may be related to processes at work deep in the earth's crust and in the underlying mantle.

To summarize, the evidence from rocks which we have considered points unmistakably to an extremely long and complicated history of the earth. As we shall see, there are different categories of evidence which corroborate these conclusions, but it is important to realize that orthodox geology is not dependent on these alone, and could in principle manage without them. In practice, of course, they greatly facilitate the study of earth history.

Evidence from fossils

The virtual omission of any reference to fossils in the preceding section was deliberate. My purpose in excluding this evidence until now was to show that the pattern of environmental changes and their approximate time-frame could be well established independent of fossils. In practice, geologists naturally make extensive use of fossil evidence, since the animal and plant communities they represent promote their understanding of the mutual interaction of environmental factors. In the earlier days of geology, when the significance of sediments and their structures was not appreciated as it is now, the dating of rocks was closely bound up with their fossil content. Now, however, geological time-measurement is no longer shackled to the same extent, and criticisms levelled against circular arguments have largely lost their validity. Geologists use fossils today to pin down as precisely as possible the positions of rocks in the stratigraphical record, and also to make correlations between different geographical areas. The method is subject to debate within geology, but only about details.

There are two matters about the fossil record I should particularly like to stress in relation to my previous account of earth history. First, the fossil content of a sediment can be used for the characterization of its depositional environment *without any reference to an evolutionary interpretation of the fossil record as a whole.* An example is provided by sedimentary reefs. In numerous places all over the world, there are extremely fine examples of reef complexes occurring in rocks of widely differing age. We have already mentioned those of Devonian age in Canada and Russia, and reefs belonging to the same period are well displayed in south-west England and Belgium. Many of these ancient reefs are barrier-type, and consist mainly of shell-secreting organisms (corals, bryozoa, *etc.*) capable of building an elaborate, wave-resistant framework essential to the development and continuance of the reefs, and creating an ecological system open to colonization by many other organisms. The reef-builders and colonizers are usually fossilized in their life positions, so that the inter-relationships of the ancient community are preserved.

This allows detailed comparisons with modern reefs. When an entire reef environment is studied, a fossil assemblage distinctive of warm, shallow water can be identified in those sediments whose lithology corresponds – by analogy with today – to deposition in lagoons, the sheltered waters between the barrier reef and the shore. On the opposite (seaward) side of the reef we find, in turn, sediments indicating deeper water and stronger currents containing the fossils of animals favouring these contrasted conditions. These sediments also contain the wave-eroded debris of the reef material. When mapped, the reefs show a linear arrangement at the boundary between shallow- and deep-water areas like that of present-day barrier reefs.

In determining the ancient ecologies associated with reef development, assemblages of fossils are clearly of much more significance than individual species. The same is true in other palaeoenvironments. Muddy sediments in the inter-tidal zone can be recognized by fossil assemblages dominated by mud-loving creatures of various kinds whose habitat was either on, or just below, the mud surface. These muds are usually burrowed extensively and heavily reworked by worm-like creatures. Fossil assemblages also indicate salinity levels, establishing the location of transitional zones between marine and freshwater areas.

Fossils commonly confirm the analysis of sediments on

other grounds. Sediments showing large ripple marks, indicative of high energy currents, may contain disarticulated and broken shells and other features related to vigorous water flow.

These are only a few examples of the relationships which exist between fossils and the depositional environment. Sometimes the picture is less simple, and there are undoubtedly pitfalls in this type of analysis. Nevertheless, there are far too many correlations to suppose a merely fortuitous connection between a sediment and its fossil content, and it is a relationship with which any alternative geological model has to reckon very seriously.

The second point about the fossil record is central to the evolutionary debate. It concerns the development of life through geological time as registered by fossil remains. As a non-biologist, I shall simply state the relevant facts and comment briefly on their possible significance for organic evolution. Before doing so, I must point out that the main theme of this chapter has been geological time and its measurement, and I hope the argument has been clear enough to disprove the accusation that geologists deliberately falsify rock ages to satisfy the evolutionist's demand for time.

What then of the fossil record? There is a progression with time from lower (though often quite specialized) forms of life, to more complex and highly organized forms. This progression is not uniform, but consists of long periods of gradual modification and adaptation of species, interrupted by short periods of dramatic change marked by the sudden appearance of new forms often accompanied by the extinction of others. There is, in fact, a remarkable parallel between the geological record derived from rocks, and the fossil record. The dramatic changes do not always coincide, though they often do. For example, mass extinctions commonly accompany severe climatic changes. Appearances and extinctions also occur on a lesser scale outside the periods of explosive change.

The term *evolution* is usually applied indiscriminately to both the gradual and sudden steps in the fossil record, and a good deal of confusion has arisen as a result. It is around the sudden and large-scale changes that the problems for evolution are sharply focused, and where the major controversy lies.

These periodical and abrupt appearances of higher forms of life are important. They imply the absence of transitional forms between major orders in the fossil record, and this is so with perhaps a few exceptions; and they also mean that the popular conception of a gradual evolution over time is quite inaccurate. How are they to be interpreted? Do they represent the instantaneous creation *de novo* of new life-forms, are they the result of a greatly increased rate of biological and genetic activity, or is there some other explanation?

A number of palaeontologists argue that abrupt changes in the fossil record stem from the rapid and vigorous take-over of some animal stocks at the expense of others, which become extinct in the way that some animal and plant species today are eliminated when man takes possession of particular environments. The theory assumes major environmental crises producing conditions more favour-able to the new forms. The take-overs are assumed to be so rapid that, given the poor chances of an organism being fossilized in any case, the sparse progenitors of these higher forms are unlikely to be preserved in the fossil record. Hence their apparent sudden arrival on the scene. However true this interpretation may be, it begs the vital question of origin. One problem for the palaeontologist here is that many ancestral forms were probably soft-bodied, and therefore incapable of preservation.

Another suggestion is that, at specific points in geo-logical time, mutations occurred at a greatly increased rate, possibly induced by bursts of cosmic radiation leading to the rapid development of new life-forms. For reasons already mentioned, the higher forms supplant some of the earlier ones, resulting in partial or complete extinction.

As a scientist, I reserve judgment on these interpreta-tions. But from a Christian standpoint, we need to acknowledge that all of nature gives proof of God's acti-vity, including natural processes. We need to ponder Professor Hooykaas' statement: 'He who is not blind to the wonder in the growth of an embryo, will not fail to recognize as much miracle in evolutionary creation as in sudden creation.' Whether we plump for a 'creationist' or 'evolutionary' explanation of the evidence is, in the long run, not so important as whether we respond to God with worship as we stand before the natural world.

Evidence from radiometric dating

Within the last two or three decades, great advances have been made in *geochronology*, the dating of rocks by radiometry. In the constituent minerals of rocks there are certain atoms (isotopes) which break down spontaneously, yielding so-called daughter atoms. Different radioisotopes decay at different rates (or *decay constants*), measurable in the laboratory. The *half-life* is the time needed for one half of a given amount of isotope to decay. Rocks are dated by measuring their present number of parent and daughter atoms and relating these to the appropriate decay constant.

Radioactive atoms in rocks thus act as a clock, recording the passage of geological time. The main radioisotopes used are those of potassium (K), rubidium (Rb), uranium (U) and carbon (C).[1] The first three decay respectively to argon (Ar), strontium (Sr) and lead (Pb), and each has an extremely long half-life. The half-life for rubidium, for instance, is 4,800 million years; by contrast, radiocarbon has a half-life of only 5,570 years.

In principle, the radiometric method is straightforward; in practice it can be difficult and complex, partly because the experimental techniques are complicated, and partly because certain assumptions have to be made which cannot be completely proved. For example, it has to be assumed that there has been no loss or gain of either daughter or parent atoms except by radioactive decay of the parent. Also, assumptions have to be made to correct for the number of daughter atoms present in the rock when it was first formed. In favourable circumstances, the necessary assumptions can be deemed reasonable, as in the Rb-Sr method, for instance.[2]

[1] In recent years, the decay of a radioisotope of neodymium to samarium has been used widely in the dating of very old rocks.

[2] See A. G. Fraser, 'Radiometric dating', *Christian Graduate*, Vol. 30, No. 4, December 1977, p. 120.

Because of the assumptions which always have to be made, the method has aroused considerable criticism, some of which I think is justified. There are, however, several tests by which the general validity of radiometric dating can be assessed, and I shall mention two here. One important test is the concordance of ages. If (within the limits of experimental error) similar ages are obtained when the same method (say Rb-Sr) is used on different minerals in the same rock, or when different methods (K-Ar, Rb-Sr) are used on one particular mineral in it, then the figures obtained may be assumed to be reliable. Such concordance is well established for various types of rocks, especially igneous rocks which have remained undisturbed after their initial crystallization. These results place the technique on a reasonable footing, since fortuitous concordance would be highly improbable.

The other – very important – test which I wish to mention concerns the extent to which radiometric dates harmonize with the relative geological time-scale I have already considered. Even allowing for some unreliable dates and for occasional lack of rigour in the practical application of principles, the pattern of ages which has emerged from radiometric studies from all over the world is impressive, both in its accord with the relative timing of geological events derived independently, and in the additional light it has shed on earth history. For instance, many of the measured igneous and metamorphic rocks in the mountain belt crossing northern Scotland already mentioned yield radiometric ages in the range of 400 to 550 million years, whereas comparable rocks in the Alps show ages of 10 to 80 million years old. These dates are consistent with the relative ages of these two mountain belts based on the different degrees to which they have been eroded.

Radiometric dates now available pinpoint specific geological events from widely scattered areas of the earth and, taken together, they reveal a fascinating pattern of recurring crustal upheavals throughout geological history. It is now clear that in *all* the continental blocks of the earth, where large areas of complex metamorphic rocks (referred to as *basement*) occur, the oldest ages exceed

3,000 million years, the oldest being 3,850 million years for rocks in Greenland. This date may be compared with the 4,500 million years found for meteorites and the oldest moon rocks. Interestingly, sedimentary rocks are recognizable in these most ancient terrestrial rocks, indicating an even older history.

Furthermore, in these basement rocks, radiometric dates cluster around particular values, demonstrating that periods of major geological activity, widely separated in time, occurred repeatedly on a world-wide scale. Radiometric measurements confirm a pattern of long periods of relative tranquillity alternating with comparatively shorter phases of heightened geological activity.

Orthodox geology by no means claims to interpret all facts about the earth within the model of earth history we have considered. But the model does interpret the bulk of the data consistently, and this suggests that a more complete explanation will not differ from it radically. All the evidence we have considered, whether from rocks, their fossil content or their radiometric dates, points to the same conclusion: that the earth is extremely old, and that its history consists of long periods of relative quiescence, separated by major revolutions embracing radical changes in environment, igneous and metamorphic activity on an extensive scale, and frequently, mass extinctions of organisms and the appearance, in the fossil remains, of new and often higher forms of life. In short, time is a built-in property of rocks, and it seems to me impossible to deny the age of the earth on scientific grounds.

Orthodox geology and other views

Flood geology
Recently there has been a revival of 'flood geology'. In the late eighteenth and early nineteenth centuries, geologists of the Catastrophist School believed that there was irrefutable evidence of a universal flood, though they would not have regarded the flood as explaining all geological

phenomena. During the nineteenth century, this view fell generally into such disfavour that even the Rev. Professor Adam Sedgwick, a Low Anglican who strongly opposed the strict uniformitarianism of Lyell and the evolutionism of Darwin, found these views untenable and even then, long before the advent of radiometric dating, believed the earth to be millions of years old.

In its modern version, flood geology seeks to account for all geological data, and reaches beyond the Noachian deluge to deal with the original creation. Its primary thesis, however, is that most sedimentary rocks on the earth's surface were deposited during, and immediately after, the great flood recorded in Genesis 7-8. Associated with this cataclysmic event were unprecedented and non-repeatable changes both in the earth's crust and in the atmospheric environment. Among other things, these changes resulted in profound modifications of world climate, especially the initiation of the great glacial period.

One of the main concerns of flood geology is to account for the fossil record. The distribution of fossils indicates a general progression from lower to higher forms of life in successively higher rock strata; this is interpreted as the result of the successive annihilation of animal communities as the flood waters rose. The more advanced animals were able to escape more readily to higher ground; consequently they dominate the upper strata. Some kind of hydro-dynamic sorting of the organisms is also believed to have contributed to the sequence of fossils.

It is clear that there are immense difficulties in trying to harmonize flood geology with the complex pattern of changing palaeoenvironments described earlier. My own considered view is that the rocks themselves, quite apart from their fossils, tell a very different story. In presenting this case, I have openly accepted that geologists are right in arguing from analogy, and in deriving from it both the mode and time-scale of rock formation. Following this method, it is impossible to reconcile the following phenomena with a single catastrophic event of short duration: continual shifts in land and sea distribution; changing topographies; the recurrence of different climatic regimes (glacial and desert periods, *etc.*); the cycles of erosion and deposition; the development of ancient soils at various times in the history of the earth; the way in which the sedimentation sequence is punctuated many times by major crustal events which folded and deformed sediments; the intrusion of hot molten rock with associated metamorphism, and much more besides.

Nor can flood geology provide a framework for predicting the location of the earth's resources in the way orthodox geology does in many cases. For example, if (as flood geology claims) the flood waters were sufficiently strong to deposit much of the sedimentary succession on the earth's surface, they would undoubtedly have had the power to remove all vegetation far from its place of growth. The vegetational debris would have subsequently ended up with sediments whose characteristics would represent the local environment of deposition, *not* the environment in which the vegetation grew. Any resemblance between the two would be coincidence. Consequently, there would be no means of extrapolating back from the character of the sediment to its environment of formation, and hence to the location of coal seams derived from the decaying vegetation. In a similar way, the distribution of diamonds and gold nuggets in sediments would bear no relation to their source rock; whereas, in fact, a close relationship can often be established and predictions made accordingly.

As to the fossil record, flood geology offers no plausible explanation for the high degree of correlation between the lithology of a rock, reflecting the environment of its formation, and its fossil content. Neither does it throw any light on other facts relating to the fossil record; for example, numerous shell-secreting organisms show progressive, small-scale changes in their external shape in successive layers of sedimentary rocks. These correlate with changes in the internal organs, and almost certainly represent adaptation to environmental changes. Whatever their cause, these modifications are impossible to justify in the turbulent conditions of a catastrophic flood. Again, there are some species (for example, primitive brachiopods) which persist without significant modification through the entire fossil record after their first appearance, whereas others (for example, many graptolites) flourish for a relatively short time, show rapid modification and occupy a very limited segment of the sedimentary record. This too seems inexplicable if all sediments are the product of a single depositional episode.

Flood geology fails to illuminate a whole range of other facts relating to the fossil record. It does not recognize the distinction between organisms fossilized in their life positions, as in reefs, and those dispersed after death. Further, it cannot account for the close correlation between the sudden extinction of fossils and major environmental changes – established by other criteria – which have occurred repeatedly in geological time. A formidable problem is also posed to flood geology by the occurrence of sediments carrying a particular fossil assemblage, later metamorphosed locally and becoming a source rock for new sediments which, in turn, have their own set of fossils. A British example of this kind occurs in the Shap area of north-west England where a very thick sequence of marine sediments, with a distinctive deep-water fossil assemblage of graptolites, was strongly folded and then locally metamorphosed by the Shap Granite. A long period of erosion subsequently planed the surface of the sediments and granite, after which new sediments began to accumulate, carrying chips of both the older sediment and granite. These younger sediments contain a very different fossil assemblage of corals and brachiopods, characteristic of shallow water.

Even within its own scheme of interpretation, flood geology does not account for particular aspects of fossil evidence. For instance, it is hard to understand why marine organisms overwhelmingly dominate the lowest part of the fossil record, especially free swimmers, which presumably could have escaped through the rising flood waters. Many other examples could be given to demonstrate the inadequacy of flood geology to explain the distribution of fossils in sediments.

In the light of these considerations, I am unhappily forced to conclude that flood geology is profoundly at variance with the geological evidence when it is analysed in detail. Even if we set aside all the dates obtained by radiometric means (which would clearly negate the model by themselves), no reconciliation seems possible with the historical record imprinted in the rocks. Indeed, the characteristics of known flood deposits would lead us, by extrapolation, to predict a sedimentary sequence very different from the one that actually exists.

These statements cannot and must not be taken as a denial of the great flood nor of its description in the biblical record. But how we interpret that event, whether local or universal, and what kind of geological evidence (if any) can be held to verify it, are separate questions.

The 'apparent age' view

Flood geology is invariably combined with a belief in a young earth, since both are based on taking the Genesis account at its literal face-value. Those who hold this position usually acknowledge the evidence for the earth's great antiquity, but believe that the antiquity is only *apparent*. Thus, they believe either that the earth was created in an already mature state, with pebbles on the seashore already smooth, for instance, or that geological processes were much faster in the past than they are today, or both. Sometimes the distinction between these views is not sharply drawn in their writings. Clearly, this view could be adopted without giving assent to flood geology.

On the apparent age view, the long sequence of natural processes envisaged by orthodox geology is replaced by *miracle*; namely the creation of a mature universe, or the speeding up of existing physical processes. This implies that the history of the earth is not accessible to scientific investigation, since this is based on the uniformity of natural law. It should be noted that literature on a young earth is not entirely consistent, because it presents miracle (for example cataclysmic events during the flood) and scientific arguments (in favour of flood geology) side by side.

The biblical record certainly contains miracles in which something is created in an already mature state. The wine at the marriage feast in Cana of Galilee (Jn. 2:1–11) is an obvious example, and there is no doubt that God could have created the universe in this way, or could have speeded up the rates of natural processes to bring the universe to maturity at an early stage. An interesting biblical incident in this connection is the budding of Aaron's rod (Nu. 17), which was found to have buds at one end, and mature almonds at the other, the apparent age varying along the length of the rod. I believe that, as long as it is separated from flood geology, it is *possible* for a Christian to hold the apparent age theory. However, I wish to argue against it strongly on the following principal grounds:

a. It seems to me to lead to an element of deception in the natural world which is not present in the miracles of Scripture. In Scripture, miracles always have an explicit purpose; furthermore, alongside each miracle there is a natural frame of reference by which the miraculous dimension can be appreciated. Some, of course, might argue that the explanation of earth history by existing natural causes could be the frame of reference by which the creative events of Genesis 1 can be judged to be miraculous. But this approach provides no basis for teaching earth history any differently from the way it is done at present, for the scientist would be perfectly correct in scientific terms to detect an age and a process which had not in fact taken place. He could not be expected to detect the sudden creation. For if the supposed creation miracles yield rocks and rock ages (radiometrically determined) which are fully compatible with present-day geological processes and their time-scale, how can they be identified in the geological record? Consequently, if we assert a six-day creation in the recent past, it must be on biblical and not scientific grounds. In which circumstances, scientific findings must be expected to appear to contradict the biblical evidence to some extent at least.

The concept of speeded-up natural processes presents much greater difficulties in the teaching of geology. For example, the cooling of a lava may occur within a few days, the crystallization of a large granite more than a million years. If we accept the time-scale for the first but reject that for the second to fit our preconceptions, there is no integrity in our science. If, on the other hand, all processes were speeded up by the same amount, the lava would have cooled in a matter of microseconds – which

A. G. Fraser

is clearly nonsense from a scientific viewpoint.

b. A more basic objection to the apparent age view lies in the strongly historic nature of the geological record; that is, the identification of specific events responsible for the end-product. The rocks at the earth's surface do not represent merely a cyclical repetition of events, about which one could extrapolate backwards to infinity without coming any nearer to a starting-point. On the contrary, a unique historical progression is preserved. This is totally different from biblical miracles involving the telescoping of time. No such history can be discovered, for instance, in the budding of Aaron's rod or in the provision of wine at Cana. The apparent age view necessitates making most of this historical record, including most fossils, the product of creation miracle instead of assigning it to real events. This raises major philosophical difficulties not only for myself, but for many other Christians.

c. Finally, the apparent age view, and the literal inter-pretation of Genesis 1 on which it is based, are not the only ways of expounding Scripture consistent with other scriptures using numerical descriptions of historical periods. The Seventy Weeks of Daniel, for example, relating to the history of God's people (Dn. 9:24–27), have never been literally verified in history despite all the ingenious schemes which have been proposed. Do we therefore abandon either the history or the prophecy? By no means. Because God is the author of history as well as the author of the Bible, as Christians we accept both accounts and humbly acknowledge our ignorance. So, I believe, should we accept both Genesis 1 and the geo-logical record. I shall return to this point in my con-clusion. It will suffice to note here that there is clearly profound mystery both in God's Words and his works.

Final comments and conclusions

I wish to emphasize two aspects of the creation-evolution disagreement among Christians, because they are crucial to the problem. The first concerns the age-old tendency to make too great a distinction between miracles and natural events, so that only miracles are thought to provide

38

evidence of God's activity: 'Except you see signs and wonders, you will not believe.' To the Christian, the whole created order is 'miracle', in the sense that everything in it goes beyond the reaches of the human mind to explain or understand in ultimate terms. This is why worship is the only appropriate response for the believer as he stands before the natural world. The great Reformers, notably Calvin (following Augustine), sought to reduce the distinction between miracles (in the sense of departure from the natural order) and natural events as much as possible, and spurned the notion that only miracles require special divine activity.

Somehow or other, we seem to have gone back to the point where only extraordinary events in nature are thought to give proof of God's activity and to vindicate the truth of his Word, whereas natural processes, capable of scientific description and explanation, are regarded as less than God-like. This is a great mistake. We simply cannot assume that God's sovereign acts are always sudden and without processes. All the events of nature express God's sovereignty, whether they are capable of scientific explanation or not. There is no reason in principle to think of a sudden creative act as more God-like than a process.

Second, God's Words as well as his works involve profound mystery. Failure to recognize this means that we are in danger of attempting to subject all biblical interpretation to mere human understanding and logic, in the same fatal way that the interpretation of nature was circumscribed by the classic natural philosophers before the rise of modern science.

In other words, we must approach God's revelation in the Bible and in nature in the same spirit of childlike submission, and not impose our own ideas upon them. Professor Hooykaas, in his splendid exposition of the history of modern science, illustrates this with reference to Pascal. He quotes Pascal's question relating to God's revelation in Jesus Christ: 'How dares such a low being [Man] assume the right to put to God the limits that his own thought imposes on himself?' He goes on to say, 'In the *same* way in science hard facts have to be accepted, no matter whether they are or are not conformable to the expectations of reason.'[3] These 'hard facts' have to be accepted, whether or not they conform to our limited understanding of the infinite truth of God and our particular interpretation of his revelation.

If the scientific enterprise was released from its bondage to human reason by the biblical view of nature and nature's God which stemmed from the Reformation and the Puritan movement, as Hooykaas believes, we need to be careful in case, in the name of biblical orthodoxy, we again place greater limits on science than are proper. The falsely based hostility of the church to Galileo's acceptance of the Copernican system of astronomy is a very unhappy historical precedent.

The Scriptures make it abundantly clear that the Lord is not conditioned by the narrow limits of the human mind (Is. 55:8–9). A pertinent passage in this context is 2 Peter 3, where the apostle is dealing with the apparent contradiction between the Lord's promise to come again quickly, and its fulfilment – a discrepancy now much greater. Peter does not suggest that man's way of measuring time is wrong, but rather that God's way of describing it may be very different from ours. There is almost an implied criticism here of those who take a literalist interpretation, trying to tie God down to their way of thinking. It seems to me, therefore, that the days of Genesis 1 are days in *God's* reckoning, like the Seventy Weeks of Daniel 9, and we may never know, nor indeed do we need to know, their counterpart on human time-scales. When proclaiming the Word of God, we must always stand by his reckoning and not our own, even though the latter is perfectly valid in its proper context. This is not to assume, however, that God's reckoning of time bears no relation to our own. For example, the Genesis record impinges on man's time-scale in a number of places, particularly in relation to the pattern of work and rest in a week (Ex. 20:8–11).

These conclusions will disappoint those who want

---

[3] R. Hooykaas, *Religion and the Rise of Modern Science* (Scottish Academic Press, 1972), p. 45 – my italics.

scientific proof of the inerrancy of Scripture. On this I have two final things to say. As Christians, whether scientists or not, we demonstrate the inerrancy and inspiration of Scripture much less by scientific argument than by the way our lives are moulded by submission to its authority and power. As for our unanswered problems, we are only following in the footsteps of Job. His problems and questions were deeper than ours, but in the end they were given no final answer. Rather, he came to see that God was God, and that is how it should be with us.

Response to A.G. Fraser

E. H. Andrews

Dr Fraser's article deals in turn with the evidence from the rocks, the fossils and from radiometric dating, before considering non-conventional approaches (such as flood geology) and presenting conclusions. This comment will follow a similar sequence.

Evidence from the rocks
My own article already covers most of this ground from the creationist viewpoint and requires no repetition here. There are, however, one or two points of detail that can be mentioned. Firstly, although Dr Fraser's treatment of this section is refreshingly free from speculation, this defect does appear at crucial stages in his argument. For example, after establishing quite fairly that 'the geologist can discriminate between geological processes occurring on very different time-scales', he adds that 'the smoothing and shaping of pebbles' must have taken 'a vastly longer time' than the duration of a single flood. But as I have discussed in my own article, such a process has been observed to occur in a matter of months on the volcanic island of Surtsey. Thus an acceptable claim, that the rocks reveal processes occurring at different rates, is transformed into an unacceptable conclusion that vast amounts of time are needed for the slower processes. Another example of this same kind of *non sequitur* is found in the suggestion that

'great variations in the thickness of the Torridonian rocks over short distances [showing that] the sediment was extensively stripped away' necessarily indicate 'a long time-gap'. Such a claim surely rests on the assumption that sedimentation and erosion were slow processes and thus represents a wholly circular argument. The article begins with the claim that uniformitarianism 'assumes only the constancy of physical laws underlying geological processes, but accepts that the processes themselves may occur at very different rates'. Yet when it becomes necessary later to press the argument we read such statements as this: 'By analogy with present rates of erosion in the Alps and Himalayas, one must infer a time interval of the order of hundreds of millions of years.' This seems to be a case of wanting to have it both ways!

My final comment under this heading concerns the claim that 'it has been calculated that more than one million years are needed to heat the sediment to a temperature consistent with the new minerals produced in it'. Since no reference is given I have been unable to check the precise nature of these calculations. Having employed heat-flow calculations in my own research, however, I am familiar with this type of prediction. It must be pointed out that several assumptions are involved, particularly the temperature of the intruding magma. It would be very easy to adjust this temperature to such a value that the time required for mineral formation was infinite, whereas a slightly higher assumed temperature would give a finite answer. The calculation also assumes that heat transfer is entirely through conduction. But if 'the heating effect. . . extends outwards for at least 2 kilometres' as claimed, the severe temperature gradients involved would probably require that the sediments closest to the magma were actually melted. This might give rise to rapid convective heat transfer. The possibility of exothermic phase changes in the sediments is also probably ignored. In short, I am very sceptical of this kind of calculation.

Evidence from the fossils
A number of questionable statements occur in this section. 'There is', we read, 'a progression with time from lower. . .

43

to more complex and highly organized forms.' This surely is a case of stating at the outset what has to be proved. The implicit equation of the stratiographical sequence and extended time is just what creationists question. In similar vein Dr Fraser writes that the 'abrupt appearances of higher forms of life. . . imply the absence of transitional forms. . . in the fossil record'. Surely they *demonstrate* the absence of transitional forms in the record rather than 'imply' such absence. Again, it is suggested that 'bursts of cosmic radiation' led to 'the rapid development of new life-forms'. This is biological nonsense, considering the lethal character of ionizing radiation and that higher forms of life are more susceptible to damage by this means than lower forms. Wisely, Dr Fraser reserves judgment at this point and turns to generalities. The fossil record has little to say about evolution and even less about the age of the rocks in which it resides.

Evidence from radiometric dating
I believe that all the substantive points covered in this section have already been dealt with in my own article.

Non-conventional approaches
The major point I wish to make here is that 'flood geology' is rather unfairly handled in this section. Such phenomena as the relation of fossil fuel and specific fossils to sediments appropriate to their life environment; the fate of free-swimming forms in a world-wide flood; and the relative stratiographic placement of different but related fossils, can all be explained by refinements of the 'flood' model. Flood geology does not require that all sediments and remains were carried, violently, far from their original environment. There are, of course, numerous examples of fossil graveyards where violent transport is apparent. Equally, however, the burial of creatures or vegetation living on well-consolidated substrates (whether terrestrial or marine) would leave those remains closely associated with their life environment unless the whole region were subsequently disturbed. The existence of different varieties of the same species coexisting at different depth contours in the same vicinity is a current ecological fact. The

massive burial of such an environment by flood sediments could produce exactly the effect normally interpreted as a gradual evolutionary change. In fact the greatest argument against flood geology is that, like evolutionary theory, it can (given a little ingenuity!) explain anything and everything. It does, however, have one thing to commend it. Namely, it is true to the biblical account of the flood as a universal phenomenon. The evolutionist is virtually forced to limit the flood to a local event, for otherwise it would have to show up in the geological column. Yet such verses as Genesis 6:11–13; 7:4, 19; 8:21; 9:19 can be understood only in terms of universality. In any case, if the flood was not universal, why did Noah have to preserve *all* life-forms, and not simply those needed for food after the flood?

Conclusions
In this section it is suggested that creationists think of God's activity only in terms of the miraculous. 'Natural processes. . . are regarded as less than God-like' by creationists, complains the author. I hope that what I have written elsewhere will demonstrate that this is very far from the case. Indeed, the providence of God can only be appreciated fully once one has grasped the distinction between providence and miracle. But what Dr Fraser calls 'the age-old tendency to make too great a distinction between miracles and natural events' must be defended. Miracles are miracles. They are not natural events, and I fail to see how we can avoid making the distinction between them! This is the essential issue. It is no disservice to science to define its limitations. Indeed, failure to appreciate these limitations is likely to bring science into disrepute and to hinder its development.

2
The age of the earth

E. H. Andrews

*Introduction · Scientific arguments against
uniformitarianism · Rate processes · Using rate
processes to date the rocks · The lesson of Surtsey · Other
evidence of a young earth · Radiometric dating ·
Transcendental considerations · Conclusion*

Introduction

Before we become involved with detailed argument, I
believe it is important to survey the matters at issue
between those who subscribe to uniformitarian geology
and those who believe the earth is relatively young. Here
I want to introduce an illustration.

Suppose I go into the garden and find a ripe apple lying
on the ground beneath my prize apple tree. The most
probable explanation is that the apple is a windfall.
However, it is not the only *possible* explanation. For
example, the apple might have been deliberately picked
by a mischievous boy and taken home. Before he could
eat it, his mother discovered what had happened and sent
him to replace the apple under the tree.

The 'windfall theory' is the more probable theory,
simply because it requires only a single unobserved event.
The 'small boy theory' requires a succession of interlocking events which are equally unobserved. The intrinsic
probability of a theory reduces as the number of
assumptions (unobserved events), which have to be
invoked, increases.

It is a general principle of modern science (derived from
'Occam's razor') that the explanation requiring the
smallest number of assumptions should always be

46

adopted. Although this explanation is seldom the only possible one, it is nevertheless the most probable and thus (by definition) the most 'true'. Thus a scientific mind would accept the 'windfall theory' rather than the 'small boy theory' to explain the fallen apple.

Uniformitarian geology is, without question, an attractive theory of the history of the earth because it involves a minimum number of assumptions. It posits, for example, a steady-state model of the earth, requiring no assumptions regarding past unobserved catastrophes. It does not need to invoke unobserved processes (whether natural or miraculous) occurring at some past era but unknown to us today. Like the 'windfall theory', it presents itself as the most probable, and therefore the truest, the most scientific, explanation of terrestrial history.

Let us, however, return to the orchard. Suppose now that I examine the fallen apple and see the imprint of a set of small human teeth. This additional evidence dramatically alters the picture, and the 'small boy theory' immediately assumes a much greater relative probability, since the 'windfall theory', *although requiring fewer assumptions*, is unable to account for all the facts of observation. We must always select the simplest explanation of a phenomenon, but never to the exclusion of some of the evidence. The most probable (truest) scientific theory is that which explains *all* the facts of observation in the simplest manner.

Standing, Newton-like, beneath our apple tree we are forced to make a choice. Either we must reject the 'windfall theory', despite its simplicity (scientists would say 'elegance'), and accept that only a more complicated explanation will suffice. Or else we may insist that the teeth-marks can somehow be reconciled with the 'windfall' theory. We might say, 'Yes, admittedly they look like teeth-marks, but that would contradict the "windfall theory" so the marks cannot be what they seem. They are probably punctures caused by marauding wasps or ants which just happen to resemble teeth-marks.' Thus we re-interpret the teeth-marks to make them consistent with the 'windfall theory'. In this instance our guiding principle

47

is that an elegant theory, which explains so much so simply, must at all costs be retained.

The creationist's complaint about uniformitarian geology is not that it lacks elegance or plausibility, but that it considerably oversimplifies the issue by ignoring or explaining away contrary evidence (the teeth-marks). This contrary evidence is of two kinds. First, there is the scientific evidence against uniformitarian geology, for example the widespread evidence of past geological catastrophe and of processes (like mass fossilization) not observable today. Second, there is the other kind of 'teeth-mark': the testamentary evidence of Scripture which, taken at its face value, teaches that the earth is young.

Of course, the uniformitarian thinker accepts that catastrophic events have occurred in the past, and that the planet's crust today is more quiescent than of old. But at the same time he refuses to allow these 'teeth-marks' to affect his basic viewpoint. He dismisses any violent episodes of geological history as mere perturbations of uniform process, and thus as irrelevant to the mainstream of geological morphogenesis. The biblical testimony is treated in a similar fashion. Instead of admitting the Genesis record as evidence bearing on the actual history of the earth, it is reinterpreted to harmonize with uniformitarian time-scales, even though, as we have discussed elsewhere in this volume, such 'harmonization' involves a plethora of special pleadings and does violence to the text.

I believe that we must squarely face the situation that the biblical testimony and the uniformitarian model of geological history stand in contradiction. I agree that there are many geological observations that are *better* explained (in our present state of knowledge) by the conventional geological theories, and that are difficult to reconcile with the model of a young earth. In many ways uniformitarianism remains the 'most probable' explanation, in the sense that the 'windfall theory' is more probable than the 'small boy theory' in our illustration. In spite of this, I believe that to cling to conventional wisdom in this matter, and to explain away contrary evidence, is a failure to observe scientific methodology which requires that *all* the evidence be allowed its full weight. If this leads to impasse or antinomy, so be it. Just as the contradictory theories of the wave and corpuscular natures of light had to be reconciled by a transcendent concept (that of quantum mechanics), so perhaps the contradictions here discussed may have to be resolved at a higher level.

In the remainder of this chapter, therefore, I want to look first at the scientific case against uniformitarian geology and its time-scale, and secondly at the possible solutions that may exist on a transcendent level (both scientific and miraculous).

Scientific arguments against uniformitarianism

Let me admit immediately that this is an area in which the proponents of a young earth tend to be on the defensive. This, however, should not be interpreted as indicating any weakness in their case, but rather that professional geologists, who have the facts at their fingertips, are likely by their very training to be espoused to conventional thinking in this field. Thus D. A. Young, in a recent book[1] recommending the 'day-age' theory of progressive creationism, constantly complains of the problems he would face in the practice of his geological profession, if he were forced to accept the mature creation theory.

The arguments for an ancient earth (aged approximately 4.5 thousand million years according to current estimate) fall into three main categories. First come the arguments from cosmogony, involving the length of time required for the earth to form from interstellar matter. I do not intend to deal with this (except later in broad terms), because we really have no agreed theory of planetary formation, and thus no acceptable model on which to base our arguments. The second category of evidence concerns the rates of formation of sedimentary rocks and other geological processes such as mountain-building and continental drift. The third type of evidence is that of radiometric dating. Let us consider the two latter in turn.

[1] D. A. Young (1977) *Creation and the flood* (Baker Book House, Grand Rapids), pp. 76–78.

E. H. Andrews

Rate processes

A 'rate process' is one which requires the passage of time for its accomplishment. The flow of heat and the deformation of fluids and solids are typical rate processes. One of the all-pervading aspects of rate processes is that the time required for a given event or transition to take place is strongly dependent upon environmental factors such as temperature and pressure. An exception to this appears to be the radioactive decay rates of unstable isotopes, which seem to be independent of most environmental factors, but even this has been questioned recently.[2] Furthermore, any bombardment of such atoms by energetic particles can vastly increase decay rates, as in a nuclear reactor or atomic bomb.

The problem therefore in assigning rates to unobserved historical processes is vast; indeed it is almost insoluble. Unless we can also assign values to the temperature, the forces that were acting, the chemical environment and so forth, it is impossible to be specific about the rate at which a given process occurred in the past. And, moreover, the differences are not small. In the deformation of solids by plastic flow, and in the flow of simple liquids, as well as in chemical reactions, the rate of the process depends exponentially upon the temperature. Thus, if a certain rise in temperature produces a tenfold increase in the rate of a process, an additional temperature rise of the same amount will increase the rate to a hundred times its original value. A third increment of temperature rise multiplies the rate to a thousand times the starting-value, and so on. Of course other events often intervene to complicate this simple picture, but the point I want to make is that processes involving chemical reaction, deformation, flow and so on, can vary in rate by orders of magnitude depending on the temperature at which they occur.

Geologists frequently appeal (correctly, in my view) to great temperature changes to account for past geological events. Metamorphic rock formations are the most obvious example in which the temperature rise was

[2] D. B. De Young (1976) 'The precision of nuclear decay rates', *Creation Res. Soc. Quarterly* 13, No. 1, pp. 38–41.

sufficient to cause crystal phase transformations including melting and recrystallization. Under such conditions the rock would have become extremely plastic and capable of high rates of deformation. Mountain ranges could be formed on the time-scale of days rather than millennia, *given* sufficiently high temperatures. Equally, non-metamorphic, sedimentary rocks could undergo rapid deformations if their lithification were incomplete. Everything depends upon the conditions prevailing at the time.

Similar considerations apply to the effect of forces on rates of deformation, erosion, deposition and so on. Thus the process of sand-blasting, in which sand particles are projected at a surface by compressed air, can accomplish in minutes a degree of erosion that might take centuries to occur by normal wind-blown grit. In the same way, jet aircraft canopies may suffer surface erosion by droplets of rain that would cause no damage whatever to a stationary object. We have all seen the amount of silt and debris that can be deposited by a flash flood in minutes, corresponding to the deposition of years under normal water-flow conditions.

Against these rather self-evident considerations it is sometimes argued that high rates of deformation in rock strata would cause fracture rather than deformation and folding as observed. Thus mountain building must, it is assumed, be an intrinsically slow process. But this is so only under certain conditions. If, for example, a hydrostatic pressure is applied to a brittle material, it may eventually become ductile; that is, it flows rather than fractures. Even without this type of 'all round' pressure, many solids are brittle in tension but ductile in compression, so that under compressive loads they actually flow. Furthermore, much depends upon the degree of lithification of a sediment. If it is still relatively 'soft' when deformed, the likelihood of flow without fracture is greatly enhanced, as also is the likely rate of erosion.

Another argument by which rates of rock formation are sometimes deduced involves the internal morphology of the strata. Water ripples in sandy deposits or the segregation of larger from smaller particles do indeed give some indication of the conditions under which sedimentation occurred. But a given morphology does not correspond to a unique rate of formation. Rather, it corresponds to a *set of conditions* in which sedimentation rate is only one of several variables. Other important variables will be the flow rate of water, its density and its viscosity. Thus, while some information can certainly be derived from morphology, it seems quite unsafe to deduce that morphological similarities between past and present sediments necessarily imply equal rates of deposition.

Using rate processes to date the rocks
From what has gone before, it is clear that we have insufficient knowledge about the conditions under which historical geological processes took place to allow us, with any confidence, to ascribe quantitative rates to them. Uniformitarian doctrine therefore makes a quite *arbitrary* assumption that geological process is, in the main, in a steady state. It is agreed that this is the simplest assumption to make and, in the absence of contrary evidence, a reasonable one. This does not however remove the arbitrary nature of the assumption. We must recognize that the steady-state model of uniformitarian geology is just that – a *model* based upon simplifying assumptions. The geological time-scale that emerges from this model is thus a *model* time-scale and has a relative but not an absolute validity.

To emphasize this point further we may cite the calculation of rock ages based on sedimentation rates. In this calculation the maximum thicknesses of all the strata in the geological column are taken. The argument is that the true depth of any deposit corresponds at least to the maximum thickness observed anywhere on earth. Where the particular stratum is shallow, or absent, this is attributed to erosion. As a result, a virgin geological column is constructed having a phanerozoic thickness of some 500,000 ft, about ten times the thickness actually observed anywhere on earth. No allowance is made for the alternative possibility, that the widely differing thickness of a given stratum might have arisen from differential *deposition* rates. Only differential *erosion* rates are permitted in this reasoning, in spite of the fact that erosion and deposition rates are obviously correlated in any given crustal zone!

This is a fine example of arbitrary reasoning, but more is to come.

The total thickness of the virgin geological column is now divided by a fixed deposition rate to give the age of the deepest sediment. What particular deposition rate is chosen? The slowest possible, corresponding to the sedimentation rates estimated today for the deep oceans, far from the silt-laden waters of the continental shelf. Surely an *average* sedimentation rate would have been more appropriate? But even more bizarre is the fact that many of the sediments concerned contain, and are indexed by, the fossils of land-based and shallow-water organisms which must have been buried at the much higher sedimentation rates appropriate to continental run-offs. The depth of silt required to bury a 10-foot dinosaur would have taken 10,000 years to accumulate at deep-ocean rates. Indeed it is hard to imagine any significant fossilization process occuring at the assumed rates of one foot in 1,000 years, since complete burial in a very short time is normally a precondition of effective fossilization. Further evidence of rapid deposition comes from fossils, such as tree trunks which penetrate several strata and show that tens of feet of rock were laid down in very short periods of time. In short, the ages of rocks calculated from sedimentation rates are at best quite arbitrary relative to real time, and at worst strongly biased to give improbably great ages.

My uniformitarian friends will protest vigorously that I am being unfair. They will say that sedimentation rate calculations were never intended to give absolute ages, and that my criticisms are rendered innocuous by the fact that the traditional geological time-scale under discussion here has been verified within relatively small margins of error by the absolute methods of radiochronology. We must examine this claim presently, but if we assume it to be true, it only makes matters worse. Granted that sedimentation calculations are demonstrably *arbitrary*, how is it that radiometric dating confirms them as basically *accurate*? Is this not a surprising result? If I mark off 100 equal but arbitrary divisions along a strip of wood, it is most unlikely that the total length will come to one metre. I might be two or three times, even ten times, too short or too long. It would be a great coincidence if truly arbitrary divisions turned out to be just one centimetre in length.

I am not here accusing anyone of fraud! However, I would suggest that, in adopting the various assumptions necessary in radiometric dating, experimenters have – consciously or unconsciously – taken the existing geological time-scale as a calibrating yardstick, tending to reject as untrustworthy any results that differ from it significantly. Documented evidence of this attitude is given later.

I have pointed out elsewhere[3] that equally realistic assumptions, using sedimentation rates appropriate to flood and inundation conditions on or near land, would dramatically reduce the supposed age of the geological column (to tens of thousands of years instead of thousands of millions). Morris[4] has listed over seventy rate processes observable today together with the age of the earth (or universe) deduced from them on the basis of uniformitarian assumptions, that is, that the rates were historically constant. The age estimates obtained vary from less than a few thousand years to 500 million years. For example, calculations based on the influx of various elements to the oceans via rivers give ages as diverse as 100 years (aluminium), 8,000–9,000 years (nickel, silicon) and 260 million years (sodium). It is obvious of course that in many cases the uniformitarian assumptions are invalid and the age obtained fictitious. Our problem is, however, to decide *which* uniformitarian assumptions are correct and which are false. I do not think that this problem has yet been solved, in spite of the confidence with which ages of thousands of millions of years are ascribed to the earth and its rocks.

[3] E. H. Andrews (1978) *From nothing to nature* (Evangelical Press, Welwyn), pp. 60–63.
[4] H. M. Morris (1974) cited in *What about origins?* by A. J. Monty White (Dunestone Printers, Newton Abbot, 1978), pp. 128–129.

The lesson of Surtsey

For a specific example of rapid geomorphological development, we may refer to the volcanic island of Surtsey, off
Iceland. It was produced during an eruption covering the
period November 1963 to June 1967. Within a period of
months this sterile, virgin rock was transformed into a
'mature' island with beaches, pebbles, sand, vegetation
and many other features which would superficially suggest
great geological age. I do not think that any radiometric
dating has been carried out, but judging from such measurements made on other recent lava flows,[5] an apparent
age of hundreds of millions of years might easily be
obtained. I am not suggesting that Surtsey proves anything
conclusively, but merely that the *appearance* of great age
or geological maturity can be vastly misleading. The
official Icelandic geologist, S. Thorarinsson, writes:

> When [geologists] in the spring and summer of 1964
> wandered about the island . . . they found it hard to
> believe that this was an island whose age was still
> measured in months, not years. . . . What elsewhere
> may take thousands of years may be accomplished
> [in Iceland] in one century . . . [in] Surtsey . . . the
> same development may take a few weeks or even a
> few days.
>
> On Surtsey only a few months sufficed for a land-
> scape to be created which was so varied and mature
> that it was almost beyond belief . . . wide sandy
> beaches . . . precipitous crags . . . gravel banks and
> lagoons, impressive cliffs grayish white from the brine
> . . . hollows, glens and screes . . . boulders worn by
> the surf, some of which were almost round on an
> abrasion platform cut into the cliffs.[6]

It is clear from this evidence alone that, *given sufficiently
large forces*, the rates of geomorphological development
may be speeded up by orders of magnitude. The validity
of the uniformitarian time-scale is thus based wholly upon

[5] S. P. Clementson (1970) *Creation Res. Soc. Quarterly* 7, p. 137.
[6] S. Thorarinsson (1967) *Surtsey: the new island in the N. Atlantic*
(Viking Press, New York), pp. 39–40. See also *Creation Res. Soc.
Quarterly* 16, No. 1, pp. 3–7 (1979).

the assumption that the forces acting historically within the earth's crust were, on average, those observed in today's generally quiescent conditions. If conditions such as those that shaped Surtsey prevailed to any significant extent during geological history, the age estimates may need drastic downward revision. The evidence of massive volcanism, tectonic processes, metamorphism and wholesale fossilization points to a turbulent rather than a quiescent environment over a significant portion of the earth's history.

Other evidences of a young earth

We here refer briefly to some other evidences that the conventional geological time-scale may be excessive. None of these constitutes proof of a young earth, but equally, they are just as convincing in their way as the evidence normally selected to demonstrate great geological age. We have already referred to the extreme variance in ages obtained for the oceans from modern rates of accumulation of various elements. Sodium gives a geologically 'respectable' age of 260 million years, whilst nickel and silicon yield 8,000–9,000 years. Yet in his well-known undergraduate monograph *Geological Time*, my former colleague Professor J. F. Kirkaldy refers to the 'sodium age' of the oceans but not to the highly discordant data from other elements.[7]

The rate of accumulation of meteoric dust on the earth's surface is estimated at 14 million tons/year.[8] On a uniformitarian extrapolation of this figure we would expect a layer of nickel/iron some 54 feet thick to have been produced during the supposed lifetime of the earth. In fact the oceans contain only some 8,000 years' worth of nickel, even assuming that it all came from extraterrestrial sources.

A similar calculation for the accumulation of dust on the surface of the moon led scientists to plan for the possibility that the moon landings would encounter a soft dust layer many feet in thickness. Only a few inches were in fact found. Yet moon rock is believed to be even older

[7] J. F. Kirkaldy (1971) *Geological time* (Oliver & Boyd, Edinburgh), pp. 46–48.

[8] H. Petterson (1960) *Scientific American* **202**, p. 132.

than the oldest terrestrial material.

It is claimed that manganese nodules on the ocean bed grow at rates which indicate a vast age for the oceans. Yet sizeable nodules have been found growing as encrustations upon modern artefacts such as vehicle spark plugs.[9] Stalactites and stalagmites have similarly been used to indicate great ages for limestone caverns, but identical structures growing at several inches per year are commonly found under bridges and other man-made constructions.

The earth's magnetic field is decaying at an observable rate. Uniformitarian extrapolation would predict that the magnetic field only 8,000 years ago was equal to that of a magnetic star (this argument is not affected by reversals of the magnetic field which could occur by rotation of the poles rather than oscillations in field strength[10]).

Of course, in all these cases, the uniformitarian assumptions may be false and the calculated ages thus invalid. But what we cannot do, in all fairness, is to select as valid only those uniformitarian assumptions which give rise to ages which fit our preconceived ideas, and reject others. The only safe conclusion is that any backward extrapolation of presently observed rates is unsafe!

Radiometric dating

Radiometric dating is always quoted as final proof that the earth's crustal rocks are, in the main, millions of years old. This is not always the case, however, and a number of instances exist where tree remains, embedded in 'ancient' sedimentary rock, have given carbon 14 dates of a few thousands of years.[11]

In the main, however, rocks dated by the three main radiometric techniques (Potassium-argon; the various lead series; rubidium-strontium) give ages from one million to several thousand million years (my). The basic reason why results *must* lie in these regions of time is that the age

[9] E. J. Lewis (1978) 'Tapping the world's deepest wettest mine', *Popular Mechanics* 150, No. 5, p. 91.

[10] T. G. Barnes (1973) *Origin and destiny of the earth's magnetic field.* Tech. Monograph No. 3, Institute for Creation Research (Creation-Life Publishers, San Diego).

[11] F. P. Beierle (1979) *Creation Res. Soc. Quarterly* 16, No. 2, p. 87.

result is dominated by the half-life of the decay process employed. To clarify this statement, consider the equation for the radiometric age (t) of a rock,

$$t = 1.4 \, t_{1/2} \log_e (1 + {}^D/_P)$$

Where $t_{1/2}$ is the half-life, D is the concentration of 'daughter' (radiogenic) atoms and P that of the radioactive 'parent' atom.

Of course, if D = 0, then t = 0 regardless of the half-life, but the logarithmic term varies only from 0.01 to 4.6 as the ratio D/P varies from 0.01 to 100; that is, the term multiplying the half-life varies only by a factor of about 500 as the D/P ratio varies by 10,000 times. Provided, therefore, that *any* daughter or parent atoms can be detected in the rock specimen (and there are practical limitations to the range of D/P ratios that can be measured reliably), the predicted rock dates are almost certain to lie in the range from one seventieth of $t_{1/2}$ to seven times $t_{1/2}$. For example, for the potassium-argon method with a half-life of 1300 my, a list of 74 dates for rocks ranging from tertiary to pre-Cambrian gave only three dates less than one seventieth $t_{1/2}$ and none greater than $t_{1/2}$.

These considerations do not, of course, invalidate the method. But they do indicate that the ages predicted are dominated by the half-life, and that the presence of *any* contaminant or non-radiogenic 'daughter' atoms will virtually guarantee a rock age of some hundreds of millions of years.

All of this would leave radiometric dating quite unscathed *if* it could be guaranteed that no non-radiogenic daughter material were present; or that if present it could be allowed for; and that no loss or gain of either P or D atoms had occurred. Unfortunately such guarantees are not possible. The detailed literature abounds with references to just such problems, many of which are quoted by Woodmorappe.[12] Waterhouse[13] for example states:

[12] J. Woodmorappe (1979) 'Radiometric geochronology reappraised', *Creation Res. Soc. Quarterly* 16, No. 2, p. 102.

[13] J. B. Waterhouse (1978) in *Contributions to the geologic time scale* (Amer. Assn. of Petroleum Geologists, Studies in Geology No. 6), p. 316.

It is of course all too facile to 'correct' various values by explanations of leakage or initially high concentrates of strontium or argon.

York and Farquhar[14] state:

> Where the results of comparisons of this sort [*i.e.* of different dating methods] disagree, it is clear that some sort of transfer of material into or out of the rock or mineral has taken place. It has also become apparent from the number of published discordant ages that disturbances of this nature are far more common than was formerly realized.

Again Davidson[15] writes:

> In practice very few uranium and thorium minerals have been found to exhibit this concordant pattern of ages and the much more common discordances ... have been facilely explained away as each investigator thought best ...

These writers, of course, still believe in the basic validity of the dating methods, and would probably argue that the majority of radiometric dates are 'true' because they are self-consistent or agree with the stratigraphical evidence. The point I wish to make here, however, is that once one admits (as these experts do) that a significant proportion of dates are in error on account of 'contamination', material transfer, isotopic equalization ('resetting of the radiometric clock') and other hypothesized events, then the question arises as to how one differentiates an erroneous date from a true one. The answer to this question is surprising indeed, for it amounts to a calibration of the radiometric clock by the stratigraphical rates. So, far from the radiometric time-scale providing an 'absolute' calibration of the geological column, we find the reverse is, in practice, the case. Lest I be accused of exaggeration at this point, I offer the following quotations from the literature:

[14] D. York and R. M. Farquhar (1972) *The earth's age and geochronology* (Pergamon Press, Oxford).

[15] C. F. Davidson (1960) 'Some aspects of radiogeology', *Liverpool Manchester Geological J.* 2, p. 314.

No stratigraphic evidence is available to confirm or deny this [radiometric] age (Wanless et al.[16]).

The internal consistency demonstrated above is not a sufficient test of the accuracy of the [radiometric] age determinations; they must also be consistent within any age constraints placed on intrusion by fossils in the country rocks (Williams et al.[17]).

The Mississippian age for sample NS–45 cannot be correct because it is grossly inconsistent with the stratigraphic position of the lavas. No clues as to apparent preferential loss of potassium or gain of excess argon 40 from this sample are in evidence from thin section examination (Carmichael and Palmer[18]).

Rb-Sr analyses of an initial group of hypersthene tholeiites were well aligned on the isochron of 270 ± 45 my. This result is incorrect since it contradicts a firm stratigraphic control of the age . . . (Compston et al.[19]).

In conventional interpretations of K-Ar age data it is common to discard ages which are substantially too high or too low compared with the rest of the group or with other available data such as the geological time scale. The discrepancies . . . are arbitrarily attributed to excess or loss of argon (Hayatsu[20]).

. . . inherent uncertainty in dating young volcanic rocks; anomalies may be detected only by stratigraphic consistency tests, independent dating techniques and comparison with the known time scale of geomagnetic reversals . . . (Armstrong[21]).

In many cases, of course, there is no available strati-

[16] R. K. Wanless et al. (1970) Geological Survey of Canada Paper 69–2A, p. 24.
[17] I. S. Williams et al. (1975) J. Geolog. Soc. Australia 22 (4) p. 502.
[18] C. M. Carmichael and H. C. Palmer (1968) J. Geophysical Res. 73, p. 2813.
[19] W. Compston et al. Geochimica et Cosmochimica Acta 32, p. 131.
[20] A. Hayatsu (1979) Canadian J. of Earth Sci. 16, p. 974.
[21] B. L. Armstrong (1978) New Zealand J. Geol. & Geophys. 21, p. 692.

graphical evidence by which to check the radiometric age, this being particularly true of pre-Cambrian igneous formations. Barton[22] comments:

> As is the case with radiometric ages determined from almost any rock unit, it is impossible to establish unequivocally that the ages reported here reflect the time of original crystallization or emplacement.

Brown and Miller[23] further:

> Much still remains to be learned of the interpretation of isotopic ages and the realization that the isotopic age is not necessarily the geological age of a rock has led to an over-sceptical attitude by some field geologists.

Such scepticism is understandable when radiometric ages are not uncommonly found to exceed the supposed age of the earth itself; for example, a plagioclase crystal dated at 4,900 my,[24] a basalt with an isochron of 10,000 my,[25] and the Pharump diabase from the pre-Cambrian of California with an isochron of 34,000 my.[26] Of course, discordant results and the rejection of aberrant data are not exclusive to geology, and can be found in other branches of natural science. Enough has been said, however, to demonstrate that radiometric dating is so frequently unreliable that practising geologists insist on using the stratigraphical record (based on sedimentation rates and index fossils) to control and calibrate the radiometric 'clock', rather than the reverse. It is thus totally misleading to claim, as many do, that isotopic ages provide an absolute time-scale, against which the standard geological column and its fossils can be checked.

These remarks apply not only to 'straightforward' tech-

---

[22] J. M. Barton Jr. (1977) *Canadian J. of Earth Sci.* **14**, p. 1641.

[23] P. E. Brown and J. A. Miller (1969) *Quarterly J. Geol. Soc. Lond. Special Publn.* No. 3 (*Time and Place in Orogeny*), p. 137.

[24] 'The Phanerozoic Time Scale' (1964) (*Geol. Soc. Lond. Special Publn.* 120s), pp. 377–378.

[25] R. K. Mark *et al.* (1974) *Geol. Soc. Amer. Abstracts with Programs* **6**, 456.

[26] J. Woodmorappe (1979) *art. cit.*, p. 122.

niques such as K-Ar, but also to the highly favoured isochron methods which appear at first sight to eliminate guesswork about the original isotopic constitution of the rock. All the examples cited above, where ages were obtained exceeding the supposed age of the earth, were deduced from Rb-Sr isochrons and it appears[27] that isochrons are just as likely to give geologically meaningless ages as are straightforward calculations. The present writer has studied the Rb-Sr isochron method in some detail and found that any whole rock containing two or more minerals with different initial Sr^{87}/Sr^{86} ratios must automatically give a false 'isochron', possibly of several hundred million years, even at zero age. The assumption that Sr^{87}/Sr^{86} ratios are identical at zero age for all closely associated minerals lies at the heart of the method and is questionable both theoretically (because of the differential mobility of the two isotopes) and experimentally (because the isotopic ratio varies widely in nature).

It will still be argued, of course, that all radiometric dates, whatever their errors, point to ages of millions of years. But these average or typical results depend on two things. Firstly, as discussed previously, we automatically factor-in ages of this magnitude by our choice of decay processes with half-lives of this order, so that *if any result is obtained at all* it is almost bound to be within two orders of magnitude of $t_{\frac{1}{2}}$. Secondly we assume a zero age condition that ensures such ages. Thus in K-Ar dating (the major method used today) it is assumed that no non-radiogenic argon is present at time zero. Yet the molten magma is known to contain significant quantities of argon, and indeed this fact is frequently appealed to in explaining aberrant K-Ar dates! It would be just as logical to assume some 'universal' finite concentration of argon at time zero, with a consequent reduction of predicted age. If the present atmospheric concentration of argon were taken as this universal, non-radiogenic content, K-Ar dating would give ages close to zero for most rocks.

---

[27] *Ibid.*, p. 102.

Transcendental considerations

None of what I have written *proves* that the earth is young or *disproves* the uniformitarian approach. All I have attempted to do is to demonstrate that, on a scientific level, the question remains an open one and that to *believe* in a young earth is logically tenable.

Our options can thus be summarized as follows.

a. Accept uniformitarian ages and interpret Scripture accordingly. In the writer's view this does violence to the biblical record.

b. Adopt the view that the earth is young, and that the geological evidence can legitimately be interpreted on this basis. This immediately harmonizes with the plain interpretation of Scripture.

c. Accept that geology does genuinely indicate an extended history for the earth and that Scripture does not; in other words, that science and Scripture do contradict each other.

This final section is concerned with the third of these options. The question to be answered is, 'Can the conflict between science and Scripture, if accepted, be resolved on a higher plane?'

The most obvious transcendental solution to the conflict lies in the theory of 'mature creation', but another possibility also exists that I will refer to as the theory of 'miraculous process'. We shall look at these in turn.

By 'mature creation' we mean the idea that the universe and its constituent parts were created with apparent ages. On this view the stars were created during the six literal days of Genesis 1, together with the wave-trains of light by which we now observe them. To the scientific observer, they genuinely appear to be billions of years old simply because they were created with that appearance. Adam was created instantly in the form of a mature grown man, with an apparent age of, say, twenty-five years, even though he did not exist the day before. Clearly, on this argument the radioactive 'clocks' used in rock-dating could have been created already 'reading' millions of years of apparently expired time.

It is obvious that 'mature creation' produces a harmony

between scientific observations, indicating great age, and the biblical account of a recent creation. Nothing in our scientific investigation would be capable of revealing which portion of the age of a geological feature represents true elapsed time and which portion represents an apparent age at 'time zero' (creation).

Clearly, a number of objections can be raised against the doctrine of 'mature creation'. The first is that the same arguments can be used to assert that creation occurred at 6 a.m. this morning and that our memories of yesterday are simply part of a 'mature' creation. Such an explanation of the 'cosmos' is really no explanation at all, since it does not advance our understanding of, or insight into, the world around us. However the Bible testifies *for* a mature creation some thousands of years ago, and thus limits our freedom to employ *reductio ad absurdum* arguments to the concept of mature creation.

The second, and major, objection lies in the element of deception that some see in the idea of mature creation. Would God mislead us into thinking that rocks are millions of years old by 'planting' evidence of age in the form of partially transmuted elements? Would he create wave-trains of light between distant galaxies and earth which contained intensity variations corresponding to super novae that never, in fact, took place? Would he confuse today's professional geologist by presenting a lithosphere consisting partly of process-generated features and partly of 'maturely created' ones which are indistinguishable, one from the other?

There is, indeed, some force in this objection, but surely not as much as is sometimes claimed. For one thing, God can hardly be charged with deception if mature creation is revealed in Scripture, as its proponents would claim. If men choose to ignore the Bible as a source of authoritative information, they may indeed arrive at false conclusions about the universe and its origin. But they can hardly blame God for misleading them! Secondly, even if men *are* misled by the evidence because they insist on a rigidly naturalistic interpretation of origins, it does not follow that God *intended* to mislead or deceive; no moral failure on his part is implied by their fallacious thinking. Finally, there are frequent examples in the New Testament of God 'hiding' the truth from 'the wise and understanding' but revealing it to 'babes' (Mt. 11:25). The fault again is laid fairly and squarely at the door of those whose 'minds are blinded', rather than at God's. The Christian should surely be suspicious when men in righteous indignation accuse God of deception!

A final objection against mature creation needs to be taken, I think, more seriously. This is that it allows too little room for that measure of process and duration in creation that Scripture itself records. Mature creation is instantaneous creation. Understood in its simplest form, it requires no process, no duration, no interactions, no labour! Yet, according to Genesis, creation, and especially creation upon earth, was a stupendous work spanning a six-day period and involving *effort* on the part of the Creator, from which in a genuine sense he *rested* on the seventh day. I agree, of course, that we use an anthropomorphism when we suggest that God toiled over creation, and yet, from the brooding of the Spirit to the forming of Eve from Adam's side, this is, indeed, the tenor of the biblical account.

These objections to 'mature creation' may be satisfied by using a somewhat different perspective which I will call the theory of 'miraculous process'. This approach shares with mature creation the assumption that the various stages of creation recorded in Scripture were indeed miraculous, in that they were incapable of occurring by natural process. Unlike 'mature creation', however, this viewpoint recognizes explicitly that natural law is the moment-by-moment word of God's power by which he upholds the cosmos, and that miraculous events occur as God changes these laws locally (in time and/or space). I have explained this concept of the miraculous at greater length elsewhere.[28]

Thus the various creative acts, subsequent to the *ex nihilo* creation itself, can be regarded as manipulations of the natural order in which events occurred, at God's command, in ways and on time-scales inadmissible in

[28] E. H. Andrews (1978) *From nothing to nature*, pp. 101–104.

terms of natural (that is, normal) law.

Thus we can envisage the emergence of dry land from the primaeval ocean on day 3 of Genesis 1, and the gathering of the waters into seas, as processes which took place much more rapidly than would be possible naturally. This could have occurred, for example, if the viscosity of water were miraculously decreased throughout the process. Similarly the creation of living creatures 'out of the ground' suggests a rapid process of chemical combination, cell formation and growth governed and controlled by the divine Logos. This is no less miraculous, of course, than the creation of an animal, fully mature, in 'a puff of blue smoke'. It does however seem to the writer to be more consonant with the strong theme of process which runs through the creation narrative, and more consistent with the use of existing non-living matter (the ground or the dust of the earth) as a precursor of the biosphere.

It is interesting to notice that the fixity of the fundamental laws of science is no longer accepted, even by scientists, with the assurance that it once was. In a recent issue of *New Scientist*, Dr F. Close of the Science Research Council's Rutherford Laboratory writes:

> It is crucial to our existence that the nuclear force is stronger than the electromagnetic force. If these forces had the same strength in the heat of the 'big bang', as some theories predict, then the electromagnetic force weakened, and the nuclear force strengthened as the Universe cooled, yielding the forces experienced today.[29]

Twenty-five years ago, some cosmologists were prepared to abandon the law of the conservation of energy and matter to allow for continuous creation and thus avoid the implications of a beginning of the universe. The idea that miraculously accelerated processes played a part in the history of the universe thus cannot be dismissed as inadmissible, even from a strictly scientific viewpoint. Dr Close's statement, for example, bears directly upon the question of historical radioactive decay rates, since these

[29] F. Close (1979) *New Scientist* (November 29th).

are intimately associated with the 'nuclear force'. A strengthening nuclear force during cosmological history would be expected to result in a slowing down of nuclear decay rates and a corresponding exaggeration of ages calculated from current nuclear half-lives.

Conclusion

We conclude that uniformitarian geology is based upon a less secure scientific foundation that is normally admitted. Radiometric dating is far more problematical than most people appreciate, and the old geological column (based upon arbitrary sedimentation rates) remains the touch-stone of geological time. This time-scale is, on scientific considerations alone, likely to be greatly exaggerated.

Although, therefore, the uniformitarian approach is the simplest, it is scientifically insecure. I therefore argue that the facts of observation are equally consistent with a 'young earth' interpretation.

The main failing, however, of uniformitarian geology is that it refuses to admit the biblical testimony that miraculous process was operative during the formation of the universe and the earth. Recent scientific thinking, though speculative, admits that even the basic laws of physics may not be immutable in time. If this line of thinking is ever confirmed it would provide independent evidence of miraculous (non-contemporary) process in nature.

Response to E.H. Andrews

A. G. Fraser

Professor Andrews tends to equate uniformitarianism with the assumption that the rates of geological processes throughout earth history are the same as those observed under the apparently more quiescent conditions of today. I would stress again that modern geology assumes only that the physical laws underlying geological processes are the same as observed now, and it readily recognizes that these processes can sometimes occur at relatively high rates – as in the formation of Surtsey.

Clearly, geologists should keep an open mind about possible changes in physical laws with time. On present figures, however, the period covering terrestrial geology (4,500 million years) is only about a third to a quarter of the age of the universe on the 'big bang' model. Thus, if the major changes in the laws of physics belong to the early phases of the 'big bang', those occurring since the formation of the earth will be relatively small. Many geologists believe radioactive decay rates to have been constant in time on the grounds that tiny radioactive minerals enclosed in other minerals produce haloes (of damaged atomic structure) whose dimensions are independent of the age of the rock in which they occur.

But if changes have taken place, it is surely mistaken to regard them as supporting 'miraculous process'. A uniform evolution in the laws of physics, corresponding to some more fundamental law, can hardly be taken as evidence of God's activity *contrary* to natural law.

The sensitivity of rate processes to the conditions under which they occur is a major point raised by Professor Andrews. In general, geologists have increasingly recognized the importance of this factor. Sediments at high temperature would undoubtedly deform rapidly, but since rocks are very poor conductors of heat, the very slow transfer of heat through them will be a determinative factor in the deformation rate. In any case, many of the strongly folded sediments in mountain belts show no mineralogical evidence of having been heated significantly, so that the argument for greatly increased rates does not apply.

Attempts have been made to establish a time-scale for the formation of folds from known physical constants for rocks, and one calculation of this kind has yielded a value of some 32,000 years.[1] Further, in most mountain belts sediments have been folded successively by several phases of deformation, each yielding its own set of characteristic structures in the rocks. The relationship between any new mineral growth to the different fold phases can be readily deduced and a detailed time sequence of events established. Consequently, there is at present neither field nor experimental evidence to suggest that mountain belts might have formed in a matter of days.

The development of Surtsey, although a spectacular phenomenon, neither violates the uniformitarian principle nor does it of itself require a revision of geological time-scales. As Professor Andrews emphasizes, rate processes depend fundamentally on all the environmental conditions prevailing at the time, and Surtsey is an excellent illustration of this. First, volcanic bombs, which are rapidly congealed lumps of molten rock thrown out in great abundance from explosive volcanoes, take the form of smooth boulders of varying size, and they would provide one source for the well-rounded beach deposits. Secondly, when lava enters sea-water, as happened at Surtsey, violent

---

[1] R. F. Cheeney (1971) 'Strain-rates, folding and cleavage', *Scott. J. Geol.* 7, 345–348.

fragmentation of the rock occurs.[2,3] Not only is the resulting incoherent material susceptible to rapid erosion, but also 'ready-made' blocks and rock particles are available for normal marine processes to yield in a very short time the beach material, gravel banks and surf-worn boulders. One has only to observe the incomparably lesser effects of the *same* agencies of erosion, acting with *equal* force on the massive, resistant, non-volcanic rocks of the north British coastline over hundreds or even thousands of years, to realize that rate processes at Surtsey are certainly not representative of all environments. Geological processes of this kind clearly occur at very different rates within a strictly uniformitarian model.

The method of applying sedimentation rates to an idealized thickness of Phanerozoic (*i.e.* post pre-Cambrian) strata in the geological column is, I agree, rather arbitrary and not reliable for determining a proper time-scale. However, Professor Andrews' alternative calculation (tens of thousands of years), which applies sedimentation rates appropriate to flood conditions, is also unsatisfactory. The following points should explain this:

a. A high proportion (probably some 70%) of the total volume of sediments at the earth's surface consists of fine silt and clay, a substantial part of which represents deposition on the sea floor. A typical recent accumulation rate for comparable sediments is 1 metre/10,000 years.[4] These clayey sedimentary rocks are commonly poor, or lacking, in fossils except planktonic types whose preservation is not sensitive to accumulation rates. Perhaps it is necessary here to correct the impression often conveyed that all Phanerozoic sediments are rich in fossils. This is far from the case; indeed, the great majority are unfossiliferous or nearly so.

[2] P. H. H. Nelson (1966) 'The James Ross Island Volcanic Group of north-east Graham Land', *Br. Antarctic Surv. Sci. Rept.* 54.

[3] J. G. Jones and P. H. H. Nelson (1970) 'The flow of basalt from air into water – its structural expression and stratigraphic significance', *Geol. Mag.* 107, 13–19.

[4] H. C. Jenkyns (1978) 'Pelagic Environments'. Chapter 11 in *Sedimentary Environments and Facies* (Editor, H. G. Reading), pp. 314–371.

b. In areas subject to flood conditions, sedimentation is never continuous, and long periods of quiescence occur between the flooding. A case in point is the example quoted by Professor Andrews of upright trees enclosed by sediment. Published work on these occurrences[5,6,7] shows that annual deposition rates were at least 10 cm. Even if the rate was far higher than this, which seems likely, the more crucial evidence concerns the deltaic environment indicated by the nature of the tree-enclosing sediments and their spatial relationships. As in modern deltas, vegetation would have flourished on the fertile silt plain long abandoned by the active channel-ways until, eventually, the channels would suddenly be redistributed with the resulting sediment rapidly engulfing the vegetation. Evidently, most of the time is registered in the 'non-depositional' phase (represented by the vegetation) and *not* in the sediments.

c. Sediments generally show evidence of a far more complex history than that implied in the simple calculation. In particular, major breaks invariably occur such as I described from north-west Scotland. These breaks in the sedimentary record vary in their significance. In some cases, they result from profound environmental changes. Younger sediments may, for example, mantle older rocks from which an ancient topography has been carved by erosion. The later sediments fill in the hollows of the old land surface, displaying great lateral variations in thickness as a result. Differential deposition rates implied in this situation are, in fact, very well documented by geologists and are very important in all palaeoenvironmental interpretations. In favourable circumstances, a major break in the stratigraphic record can be proved to represent at least one complete cycle of deposition and

[5] F. M. Broadhurst (1964) 'Some aspects of the palaeoecology of non-marine faunas and rates of sedimentation in the Lancashire Coal Measures', *Am. J. Sci.* 262, 858–869.

[6] F. M. Broadhurst and D. Magraw (1959) 'On a fossil tree found in an opencast coal site near Wigan, Lancashire', *Lpool Manchr Geol. J.* 2, 155–158.

[7] F. M. Broadhurst and D. H. Loring (1970) 'Rates of sedimentation in the Upper Carboniferous of Britain', *Lethaia* 3, 1–9.

erosion. In the Scottish island of Arran, the youngest sediments present appear to be the widely distributed continental red sandstones of Triassic age. However, younger, fossiliferous, marine sediments, including chalk, occur as huge blocks in a large volcanic caldera. Obviously, these marine strata must have formerly covered all the Triassic sandstones on the island but were subsequently stripped off by erosion. The accidental preservation of the marine sediments by their dropping into the caldera and their subsequent shielding from erosion provides a vital clue to the actual history of events.

Some possible misunderstandings need to be cleared up on radiometric dating. The Phanerozoic time-scale immediately prior to the use of radiometric methods was believed to be approximately 100 million years.[8] Radiochronological data dramatically stretched this age to some 600 million years, so there is no question of arbitrary sedimentation calculations being accurate in any absolute sense. Rather, it is the *chronological ordering of events* established from standard stratigraphic methods that has been confirmed as correct by the radiometric dating.

The use of radiometric methods to date rocks needs to be set against the background of the varying complexity of the geological history of different rocks, as adduced by considerations of other kinds. The fact is that, for rocks which, by other criteria, have had a straightforward history, good concordances are often obtained between the dates given by different methods. As I have argued elsewhere,[9] coincidences would occur only if the various uncertainties in the radiometric methods (for example the estimation of the amount of non-radiogenic daughter material in the rock) work in the same direction for the different methods, to degrees corresponding to the different half-lives of the isotopes employed. That discrep-

[8] L. R. Wager (1964) 'The history of attempts to establish a quantitative time-scale'. P. 16 in 'The Phanerozoic Time-Scale' (Editors, W. B. Harland *et al.*), *Q. Jl Geol. Soc. Lond.* 120S.

[9] A. G. Fraser (1977) 'Radiometric dating', *Christian Graduate* 30, 120–127.

ancies should commonly occur in more complex geological situations, and be reported in the literature, is not surprising. As in medical diagnosis, when a patient's condition derives straightforwardly from a single cause, diagnosis is relatively precise. In more complicated cases, diagnosis becomes less certain. Failure to make correct diagnosis in these cases does not, however, render the methods used completely invalid, only imperfect.

I agree, nevertheless, that even from rocks with an apparently simple history, anomalous dates have been found. But in assessing the validity of radiometric ages, it is important to appreciate how they are interpreted in relation to the stratigraphic column. As already indicated, the sedimentary record is never complete at any one locality and varies considerably in its preservation from place to place. Radiometric dates have been initially calibrated from the relatively more complete sections of specific parts of the stratigraphic record from different parts of the world, and it is from these that a generally consistent pattern of ages has been obtained, providing an acceptable datum. Anomalous ages, and ages not subject to close stratigraphic control have to be seen in this light. The procedure for accepting or rejecting ages is not quite as arbitrary as believed by Professor Andrews and quotations out of context can be rather misleading.

It is worth repeating here (ref. [9]) that the half-life of Rb^{87} was initially calculated from the amount of Sr^{87} in minerals present in different rock units from which concordant U-Pb ages had been obtained. The half-life was remarkably close to that subsequently measured in the laboratory, a finding which surely refutes the charge of arbitrariness. To quote Hooykaas, 'The fact that uniformitarian theories are not contradicted by [radiometric] methods, is one of the strongest indications that, in general, they are largely conformable to reality.'[10]

Professor Andrews' illustration of the apple is, I believe, unfair. By calling the marks 'teeth-marks', the 'windfall theory' is made to look absurd. A better illustration would

[10] R. Hooykaas (1963) *The Principle of Uniformity in Geology, Biology and Theology* (E. J. Brill, Leiden), p. 162.

be a bruised apple, with marks that might just possibly be teeth-marks. The 'windfall theory' is then more reasonable, and its need to invoke hungry wasps or ants is balanced by the need to say on the 'small boy theory' that the boy dropped the apple in hurrying from his crime.

Finally, Professor Andrews' comments on mature creation are important. Since, as he says, mature creation requires no process and no duration, it also implies that the earth has no real history. Such a conception is contradicted by the days of Genesis 1 which, at the very least, emphasize the *historical* character of creation. A progressive sequence is clearly taught in the creation account that can be shown to harmonize in a general way with the earth's history as deduced from geology. Interestingly, it has been argued that the impact of Genesis 1 on believing geologists of the early nineteenth century was to induce a historical dimension in their thinking which contrasted with the a-historical geological theories of Hutton and Lyell and which indirectly prepared the way for evolutionary theories.[11] This historicity perhaps underlines the real significance of the days of creation. For the present, I see no reason in principle why they must be taken in a literal sense, not least because in the teaching of our Lord himself (the Word made flesh), figure was constantly employed and literalist interpretations inappropriate (*e.g.* Mt. 16:6–13; Jn. 3:3–5; 6:51–58, *etc.*).

A crucial question arising from this is whether we should seek to interpret any passage of Scripture in a way that flies in the face of the weight of external evidence bearing upon it. Obviously, as this volume has shown, Christians differ considerably on their approach to this question, and there is good room for argument. But the fact that Professor Andrews devotes his final section to a defence of the idea of 'mature creation', and to putting forward a modified version of it to harmonize geology with a literal six days is, I think, significant. As Ramm has pointed out,[12] the view that the earth's great age is

[11] *Ibid.*, p. 146.
[12] B. Ramm (1955) *The Christian View of Science and Scripture* (Paternoster Press, Exeter), p. 134.

only apparent is tantamount to an admission that the case in favour of an orthodox interpretation of the geological record is a very good one.

3
'I believe in God ...
Maker of heaven and earth'

R. J. Berry

*God's activity and natural processes · Explaining divine
activity · Evolution as a scientific theory · The mechanism
of evolution · The fact of evolution · Man and
evolution · Inferences · Conclusion*

Non-Christians find it difficult to understand why some
Christians argue so vehemently about evolution. Indeed,
the continuing controversy has undoubtedly been a
stumbling-block in evangelism, since many who are not
Christians regard the wrangling as a sign that Christians
are out of touch with reality and that the Christian God
is irrelevant to the problems of everyday life.

It is therefore all the more important to determine, first,
what agreement there is between all Bible-believing Christians; and then to identify where, and why, Christians
disagree.

God's activity and natural processes

Acceptance of the general scientific understanding of the
origins of life and man (which does not, of course, imply
necessarily accepting every belief of every scientist) raises
a number of problems for Christians, notably concerning
the meaning of man being created in God's image, and
how the fall affected life on earth. However, the most
important question to be faced is: from a biblical point of
view, can God's supernatural actions be brought about by
processes which we can discover?

The answer to this is clear: there can be very few Christians, whatever their views about evolution, who doubt

that their God is able to intervene in their world – and indeed that he not only can, but does.[1] To a Christian, the leading of the Jews throughout Old Testament times, the working of the Spirit in the church and the individual, and, above all, the incarnation and redeeming work of Jesus Christ himself are facts which seem to make intervention impossible to deny. The most notable example is the birth and physical development of Jesus Christ. His conception was entirely supernatural, but the whole of his development in the womb, his birth and subsequent physical growth to manhood were, as far as we know, entirely 'natural'. That is to say, they followed normal processes. Ironically it was Jesus' opponents who objected to the notion that God might have used these: 'We know where this man comes from; and when the Christ appears, no one will know where he comes from' (Jn. 7:27). They could not accept that Jesus was supernatural, since he was so obviously natural; after all, they knew his parents and brothers and sisters.

If we agree that God intervenes in his world, then the next question that arises is this: does he always 'break in' from outside, suspending the normal workings of the universe? Or does he also use processes and mechanisms which we can discover by enquiry?

This question is often avoided by making an assumption that knowing the immediate *cause* of an event automatically excludes divine involvement. For example, 'seed-time and harvest' or recovery from disease are nowadays accepted as the province of agricultural botany and medicine respectively. God may 'help' in answer to prayer, but most people (including many believers) would regard invoking him in matters of food and health as irrelevant pietism or, at best, an insurance policy. To put it bluntly: knowing how something works seems to remove the necessity for faith. The effect of this is that advances in science progressively confine God to the ever-decreasing gaps in knowledge.

No Christian can be happy about this conclusion.

---

[1] J. Houston (1979) *I Believe in the Creator* (London: Hodder and Stoughton).

However, it is relatively easy to rebut; most events have several causes, and to identify one does not exclude others. For example, as Donald MacKay points out,[2] to explain a painting in terms of the chemistry and distribution of pigments does not explain away the artist who designed and executed the picture.

However, there are some who regard such an explanation as inadequate. Among them are those who deny that biological evolution has occurred, since they believe that to accept it would deny the doctrine of God's sovereignty over creation. Here the crucial postulate is no. 3 of the 'Opening Theses' prefacing this book: 'If God chose to use processes to complete his creation, it was still his sovereign act... The events of nature represent God's sovereignty, whether they are subject to scientific explanation or not.' We shall deal first with this, then turn to consequent scientific and theological problems, and finally discuss the implications for our faith.

Explaining divine activity

Very rarely in Scripture is there any indication of the method God used to achieve his purpose. One exception is Exodus 14:21–22, where we read that 'the Lord drove the sea back by a strong east wind all night, and made the sea dry land, and the waters were divided. And the people of Israel went into the midst of the sea on dry ground. ....'. The actual site of the Israelite crossing is uncertain, but at the traditional place, near the northern end of the Gulf of Suez, the water has been blown 'back' several times in recorded history. The prevailing wind in Egypt is from the west, and an east wind is very unusual. Thus God's intervention in this case, although certainly providential, involved natural processes. Notwithstanding, it was truly a miracle. It involved a disturbance of the normal pattern of events by God in such a way as to draw attention to himself; the miracle lay in the place and timing of a physical event, not merely in the fact of its occurrence.

[2] D. M. MacKay (1960) *Science and Christian Faith Today* (London: Falcon) and (1974) *The Clockwork Image* (London: IVP).

The mechanisms producing the plagues of Egypt are not given in the Bible, but all of them could have a perfectly reasonable natural cause: deposits from upstream lakes not infrequently stain the Nile flood-waters a dark reddish-brown colour similar to blood; they stir up flagellates toxic to fish; prolonged flooding can lead (and has done so) to enormous numbers of frogs and biting insects; flies often transmit epidemic diseases of domestic animals ('all the cattle of the Egyptians died'); locusts and sand-storms ('darkness') are common in the Near East. In situations like this it is fairly easy to suggest how God might have worked. The point of the story is not simply to state God's control over the natural world – that is implicit throughout Scripture and is one of the main inferences from the creation accounts in Genesis – but to emphasize his care for his own people and his response to specific prayer.

In most cases, we know no apparent mechanism for particular miracles. For example, it is not clear why the Jordan should be more effective in healing leprosy than 'Abana and Pharpar, the rivers of Damascus' (2 Ki. 5:12), or why Christ used a clay ball to rub the eyes of a blind man (Jn. 9:6). If a modern pathologist had been present at any of the healing miracles he could in principle have described the histological changes that took place in the diseased cells of the sufferer as they became healthy, although he would not have been able to say *why* the changes were taking place. Whether we are able to say anything or nothing about the way a miracle was brought about is irrelevant to the purpose of the miracle, and does not affect or detract from the sovereignty of God. A causal explanation is usually on a different level from an explanation which describes divine activity.

It is sometimes asserted that by definition a miracle must happen instantaneously, and in particular that the *fiat* framework of Genesis ('God said . . . let there be . . . and God saw that it was good') shows that the creation miracles have no time element. This assumption involves a confusion: God is outside time, so it is irrelevant to apply our time-scales to him. From the human point of view it is clear that miracles may take some of our time to complete their effect. A particularly clear example of this is Christ's healing of the blind man recorded in Mark 8:23–25, when sight was restored gradually ('He spat on his eyes . . . and (the man) looked up and said, "I see men; but they look like trees, walking." . . . Then again he laid his hands upon his eyes; and he . . . was restored, and saw everything clearly'). Another example is the feeding of the Israelites in the wilderness – manna was provided every day.

The question of time from the point of view of creation is highlighted by considering the Hebrew word *bara*, which is commonly taken to refer to a *special* act of God in creation, in distinction to the word more commonly used in the creation narrative, which has the implication of moulding existing material (in the way that a potter moulds clay: Je. 18:3–6). In Genesis 1, *bara* is used to describe the origin of matter (verse 1), animal life (verse 21), and man (verse 27; 5:1). It is used in Isaiah 42:5 in a similar way ('God, the Lord, who created the heavens') while in Isaiah 43:1 it refers to the chosen people, a miraculous work which had taken centuries ('Thus says the Lord, he who created you, O Jacob'). Psalm 19 and other great psalms of worship of the creation marvel at the regularities of nature (which science assumes and describes), just as much as the things that are irregular. In other words, the 'everyday' processes of God are just as much his handiwork and his creation as the unusual and unexpected things he does. It is therefore inconsistent to insist that the word used for creation in Genesis 1 necessarily means something without process; conversely, we cannot argue as a matter of principle that an event which uses a known process (such as evolution by natural selection) is *necessarily* less the work of God than something that did not.

A very similar conclusion follows from Francis A. Schaeffer's consideration of Genesis 1. He admits that:

As a younger Christian, I never thought it right to use the word *creation* for an artist's work. I reserved it for God's initial work alone. But I have come to realize that this was a mistake, because, while there is indeed a difference, there is also a very important parallel. The artist conceives in his thought-world and then he brings forth into the external world. . . . And it is exactly the same with God. God who existed before had a plan, and He created and caused these things to become objective.[3]

In other words, we must distinguish between *why* God created (which is described in the Bible) and the objective *cause*, which is the role of science.

Schaeffer goes further when he discusses time in the early chapters of Genesis. He points out that time is not used chronologically in these chapters, nor are genealogies complete or even in the expected order. He is emphatic in his conclusion:

> In regard to the use of the Hebrew word *day* in Genesis 1, it is not that we have to accept the concept of the long periods of time that modern science postulates, but rather that there are no clearly defined terms upon which at this time to base a final debate. . . . Prior to the time of Abraham, there is no possible way to date the history of what we find in Scripture.[4]

He quotes B. B. Warfield as asserting: 'It is to theology, as such, a matter of entire indifference how long man has existed on earth.'

The question remains, of course, whether the creation of the world was *in fact* sudden or gradual, but we are in error if we insist *in principle* that creation in six days of 24 hours is any more consistent with God's nature and his supernatural power than creation over a long space of time. Genesis 1 does not state or deny either possibility. However, if we look at such facts as we can discover from examining the world, we have to accept that things are not as they were when the world was first created: in the past there were very large reptiles (dinosaurs) and now there are none; there used to be vast forests made up of

[3] F. A. Schaeffer (1973) *Genesis in Space and Time* (London: Hodder and Stoughton), p. 27.
[4] *Ibid.*, pp. 156, 124.

kinds of trees and ferns that do not now exist (except as coal beds); new volcanic islands have appeared; river valleys have been deepened, and so on. The changes are due to processes of some kind or another, even if they have operated faster in earlier times than now, and even if they involved catastrophic events like a great flood. In other words, it is difficult to avoid the conclusion that God has used at least some natural processes to bring the world into its present state. We must retain open minds about the speed and time of his methods if we are to be faithful to Scripture.

In summary, Scripture is clear on three basic principles:

1. God involves himself in human life and natural processes, especially in response to prayer.

2. Sometimes we know how God intervenes in order to work his will (that is, the mechanisms he uses), but our acceptance of his control is not affected by any knowledge of the way God has worked. After all, it is 'by *faith* we understand that the world was created by the word of God' (Heb. 11:3).

3. Since God is sovereign over his creation, sometimes he uses processes we can investigate by scientific methods, while on other occasions he may use mechanisms which are entirely supernatural and inexplicable in twentieth-century scientific terms.

It is important to recognize these principles, and equally important from the Christian point of view to refuse to limit God by prescribing that he *must* irrupt into his creation by irrational processes. Too often the evolution controversy has been confused by propositions that are not found in Scripture. Years ago Douglas Spanner[5] pointed out that Scripture has to be interpreted as rigorously when dealing with the evolution issue as with any other exegesis: we have to seek for the purpose of every passage, its language (literal, phenomenological, poetic, metaphorical, *etc.*), its meaning to its original readers, and its logic. Spanner argued that scientific knowledge is like a map which does not 'account for' the countryside, nor does it prove that God has created the countryside.

[5] D. C. Spanner (1965) *Creation and Evolution* (London: Falcon).

Although the biblical writers knew nothing of Newton's laws of motion, Mendel's laws of heredity, nor any of the other laws of science, nonetheless they describe a framework 'perfectly able to accommodate these laws and the outlook they represent'.

Spanner's conclusion (and one in which I concur entirely) is that:

> The biblical view is not that God made an elegant mechanism (like a super-clock) and then retired to a distance to watch it perform according to built-in laws; but rather that He remains immanent in His creation, personally energizing on a moment-by-moment basis all its multifarious happenings. He 'causes the grass to grow' (Psalm 104:14), 'makes the hinds to calve' (Psalm 29:9), and 'sends rain' (Matthew 5:45) (notice the present tenses). It is in this way that the Bible accounts for the regularity of Nature, which we loosely express by saying that similar causes always produce similar effects. This regularity is not due to the perfection of a mechanism, but to the faithfulness of God.[6]

I have laboured the point about the relation between God and his creation, but unless it is clear, any Christian discussion about evolution *per se* is liable to go awry: God is sovereign, his methods of creation are his, and the ways he controls his world are his alone. If we approach the evolution controversy with presuppositions about how God ought to work, we may well come to completely erroneous conclusions.

Evolution as a scientific theory

Is the commonly accepted scientific view of the world as arising from long-continued evolutionary change reconcilable with Scripture, or fundamentally opposed to it? My answer is that evolution is the method God used to fulfil his purpose. Later we shall look at the evidences for the *mechanism* of evolution, and for the *fact* that evolution

[6] *Ibid.*, p. 23.

has occurred, but it is relevant at this point to deal with objections that are raised by Christians and by philosophers about evolution in general.

a. The interpretation of Scripture. As Christians we accept the authority of Scripture, but we must continually beware lest our *interpretation* of Scripture be influenced by secular notions. We shall return to this point later, but it is pertinent here to recognize that a static, young, and earth-centred universe was as basic to mediaeval science as evolution is to ours; we have to beware about importing trans-cultural (including scientific) ideas into our scriptural interpretation. This is often difficult, and we must face up to our proneness to rationalize interpretations we have developed on other grounds. We may have to accept that devout Christians can accept whole-heartedly the truth and authority of the Bible, yet differ considerably about the meaning of particular passages. As Schaeffer emphasizes:

> We must remember the purpose of the Bible: It is God's message to fallen men. . . . The Bible is *not* a scientific textbook if by that one means that its purpose is to give us exhaustive truth or that scientific fact is its central theme and purpose. Therefore, we must be careful when we say we know the flow of history: we must not claim, on the one hand, that science is unnecessary or meaningless, nor, on the other hand, that the extensions we make from Scripture are absolutely accurate or that these extensions have the same validity as the statements of Scripture itself.[7]

b. The philosophical status of the theory of evolution. Uninformed readers are often confused by philosophical discussions about the nature of evolutionary theory. Three assertions are made which need refuting:

1. *Evolution is 'only' a theory.* The word 'theory' is used in a technical way by scientists. They distinguish between a set of ideas which are put forward for test, which they call a 'hypothesis', and the accumulated synthesis of tested hypotheses, which is a scientific 'theory'. A theory in this scientific sense is an established

[7] F. A. Schaeffer, *op. cit.*, p. 35.

interpretation of facts, and is thus quite different from the speculative rationalizations which are called theories in detective novels. A valuable theory combines a host of observations and conclusions into a single whole (and is sometimes called a *paradigm*), and may incorporate some apparent anomalies which are tolerated for the sake of the synthesis (just as physicists accepted Newtonian mechanics although the perihelion of Mercury never fitted the predictions); and suggests experiments and tests for further research. The accusation by some authors that evolution is *only* a theory betrays an ignorance of scientific language; when a biologist talks about evolutionary *theory*, he is referring to a corpus of ideas as firmly grounded as any other in his field.

2. *Evolution is survival of the fittest, which is tautologous.* The objection here is to the Darwinian mechanism of evolution, rather than to the fact that evolution has occurred. The argument is that natural selection is the survival of the fittest, but it is the fittest which survive (and reproduce); which is true, but trite. This is another misunderstanding about words: 'fitness' in biology is a measure of reproductive success rather than of overall health and vigour, and involves inherited traits which contribute to this success. If these traits are not possessed by all individuals (that is, if variation exists), survival will not be random and will lead to evolutionary change. The claim that natural selection is tautologous amounts merely to a failure to appreciate the factors involved in fitness.[8]

3. *Evolution is non-falsifiable and therefore not a true scientific theory.* The key name associated with this criticism is Karl Popper, who has argued that a scientific theory must be falsifiable, and Darwinian evolution is not falsifiable. There is nothing (it is claimed) which can refute evolutionary theory. For example, the widespread occurrence of organic adaptation is central to Darwinism, but no matter how grotesque or abnormal, the Darwinian can always think up an adaptive evolutionary analysis. This is fair comment: as Maynard Smith has pointed out, 'There

[8] R. H. Brady (1979) 'Natural selection and the criteria by which a theory is judged', *Syst. Zool.* 28, 600–621.

is a real danger that the search for functional explanations in biology will degenerate into a test of ingenuity.'[9] However, the fact that speculation has been over-used in evolutionary studies (especially in reconstructions or interpretations of behaviour) does not in itself invalidate the studies (Thesis 9). Indeed, it needs to be emphasized that adaptive or functional explanations are as capable of being experimentally tested as any hypothesis. It is not true that natural selection (or survival of the fittest) is an uncheckable idea. There are many cases where natural selection has been detected (and measured) under natural conditions, and then confirmed by appropriate laboratory experiments: the classical example is Dobzhansky's work on third chromosome inversions in *Drosophila pseudo-obscura*; other examples are the influence of camouflage and warning colouration on survival; of pesticide resistance in rats, mosquitoes, aphids, *etc.*; of cyanide production and tolerance of heavy metals by plants; of dark pigmentation in ladybirds and land snails living in cloudy areas; and many others. There is no great difficulty in identifying the influence of evolutionary forces acting under describable conditions, although there is a recurring research problem in recognizing which characters are affecting fitness themselves, and which are merely markers developmentally or genetically linked to the adaptive trait. This is the explanation of statements by notable biologists such as Simpson, that 'the fallibility of personal judgment as to the adaptive value of particular characters is notorious'; or Dobzhansky, that no biologist 'can judge reliably which "characters" are neutral, useful, or harmful in a given species'. Simpson and Dobzhansky are not in any sense doubting the efficacy of natural selection, but only the prospects of identifying the traits involved in particular adaptive adjustments.[10]

[9] J. Maynard Smith (1978) 'Optimization theory in evolution', *A. Rev. Ecol. Syst.* 9, 31–56.

[10] R. J. Berry (1979) 'Genetical factors in animal population dynamics', in *Population Dynamics*, edited by R. M. Anderson, B. D. Turner and L. R. Taylor (Oxford: Blackwell), pp. 53–80; B. C. Clarke (1979) 'The evolution of genetic diversity', *Proc. R. Soc. Lond.* B. **205**, 453–474.

Evolutionary theory is non-scientific in Popper's sense only if certain restrictive definitions about the nature of science are accepted. Philosophers of science argue about the validity and relevance of these definitions. For example, modern evolutionary studies are predictive only in a very limited way. On the other hand, they share similar observational and experimental approaches with other sciences, about which no philosophical doubts are raised. From the point of view of the practising scientist, evolution is as firmly based a science as, say, astronomy or parasitology.

The interpretation of Scripture and the philosophy of science are strange bedfellows, and the only reason for linking them here is that Christian anti-evolutionists frequently cite the philosophers to support their particular understanding of the creation narratives. The claim that evolution is not a science is based on a misunderstanding of the concepts and approaches of those who study evolution, and to use a secular misunderstanding to back up a disputed interpretation of Scripture is clearly hazardous.

Evolution is a science, but there is much that is called evolution which is not science; it should perhaps be called 'evolutionism'. It therefore becomes doubly important to understand the real nature of biological evolution in the strict sense. The following two sections are devoted to this.

The mechanism of evolution

The suggestion that evolution has occurred has been advanced repeatedly over many centuries, but until Darwin put forward his ideas of a possible mechanism, the possibility never gained widespread acceptance. It is historically reasonable, therefore, to distinguish between the *fact* and the *mechanism* of evolution. In North America, Darwin's theory is often referred to as the *special theory* of evolution in distinction to the *general theory*, which is concerned with the evidence for the fact of evolution.

In the *Origin of Species*, Darwin drew two conclusions from three facts:

Fact 1: All species have a large potential for increase, that is they are capable of increasing very considerably in numbers.

Fact 2: The numbers of all species remain approximately constant.

CONCLUSION 1: There must be a 'struggle for existence', for many of those born fail to reach maturity.

Fact 3: Organisms vary, and much of this variation is inherited.

CONCLUSION 2: A variant which results in its possessors leaving more offspring than do organisms lacking it, will increase in frequency. This is natural selection.

This argument appears so self-evident that it was not subjected to experimental test for several decades, and various discussions which arose about it have tended to persist in non-biological literature, without the solutions being given. The most important problems occurred following the development of genetics after 1900. Darwin himself knew nothing about the laws of genetics or the physical basis of heredity, and devised his own theory, based on *pangenes* produced in tissues throughout the body and consolidated into the reproductive cells before breeding. Following the rediscovery of Mendel's work, it quickly became apparent that naturally-occurring mutations (which are the ultimate source of all inherited variation) seemed to be invariably deleterious, recessively inherited and large in effect; in contrast, palaeontological change tends to be gradual and progressive, while 'normal' or wild-type characters are dominantly inherited. Palaeontologists and geneticists seemed to be studying two different sorts of variation.

This impasse persisted for over thirty years. Natural selection was seen by many of the early geneticists, particularly Morgan and Goldschmidt, as an entirely negative process which served merely to eliminate unfit deviations.

Genetics apparently had nothing to say about the nature of gaps between species, the origin of evolutionary novelty, the formation of higher (that is, supra-specific) categories, or the integrated nature of evolutionary change. In the 1920s the palaeontologist, Osborn, and the taxonomist, Rensch, both distinguished evolution by mutation (that is, by discontinuous jumps) from evolution by speciation (that is, by gradual, continuous genetic change). In 1932, Morgan could assert that 'natural selection does not play the role of a creative principle in evolution'.

Then within twelve years (1936–47) scientists who had previously held different views about evolution came to a common mind. This event became known as the 'neo-Darwinian synthesis'; it was largely summarized in Julian Huxley's *Evolution: the Modern Synthesis*, published in 1942. It was not the result of one 'side' being proved right, and the others wrong; but of 'an exchange of the most viable components of the previously competing research traditions'.[11] It involved three steps:

1. *The removal of objections to the compatibility of Darwinian evolutionary theory and Mendelian genetics*, largely through an increase in understanding of the inheritance of continuous variation; and the demonstration that those two sets of ideas were complementary. This came mainly through the work of the geneticists, Fisher, Haldane and Wright.

2. *The recasting of these ideas in terms of populations rather than 'types'*, thus taking account of the existence of variation and the wrongness of the classical, static notion of species.

3. *The recognition that ideas coming from a range of disciplines require these concepts for their own development.* This was realized independently by specialists working in their own disciplines: Simpson in palaeontology, Rensch and Mayr in biogeography and systematics, Huxley in zoology, Waddington in embryology, Stebbins in botany, and so on.

This is not the place to analyse the factors that brought

[11] E. Mayr and W. B. Provine (1980) *The Evolutionary Synthesis* (Cambridge, Mass.: Harvard U.P.).

the synthesis into being.[12] Suffice it to say that the main element was a better understanding of the nature and maintenance of variation in populations. A key element was Fisher's hypothesis of the evolution of dominance, which argued (and was soon backed up by experimental evidence from Ford, Harland and others) that mutant genes are not inevitably deleterious and recessive, but that genetical dominance arises through natural selection of modifying genes which increase the expression of advantageous traits in heterozygotes (and in the same way recessivity is produced by the selection of a reduced expression of deleterious traits). This is a complicated notion involving a recognition that the possession of a gene is not the same thing as the manifestation of the trait determined by that gene, and that genes interact to produce characters which are subject to natural selection;[13] but it shows how wrong is the oft-repeated statement that virtually all mutations are detrimental to their carriers.

The importance of the neo-Darwinian synthesis is that it re-established the unity of biology which Darwin's ideas had originally provided, and thus made possible generalizations within an otherwise impossible diversity of living organisms. The Periodic Table gives a similar service to chemistry. It is this unifying element which apparently makes evolution into something more than a simple scientific theory, and allows such diverse topics as fossil sequence, gene frequency changes and polymorphism, extinctions, adaptation, and so on, to be brought within a single umbrella. There may be disagreement about the interaction or relative importance of particular mechanisms, but there is no viable scientific alternative to Darwinian evolution for understanding nature. This is a strong claim, but it is why biologists tend to be unimpressed with the philosophical (or, for that matter,

[12] Details can be found in G. S. Carter (1951) *Animal Evolution* (London: Sidgwick and Jackson) and E. Mayr and W. B. Provine, *op. cit.*

[13] See R. A. Fisher (1928) 'The possible modification of the response of the wild type to recurrent mutations', *Amer. Nat.* 62, 115–126; and P. M. Sheppard (1975) *Natural Selection and Heredity*, 4th edn. (London: Hutchinson).

creationist) criticisms discussed above. Evolutionists are as willing as any scholars to discuss the correctness of their interpretation of particular data, but at the same time they tend to dismiss apparent difficulties as trivial; this is not a consequence of being brainwashed, but a sober judgment on order in the whole world of biology.

However, there are three points worth making before leaving the subject of evolutionary mechanisms:

1. *A small but significant proportion of newly-arisen mutations are advantageous to their carriers.* Concern about the genetic effects of radiation has led to an enormous amount of research into the effects of new mutation. This has shown conclusively that some mutants are favourable, and in experiments where new mutations are induced at a high rate of radiation or chemicals, these may virtually offset the effect of the majority of mutants which are unfavourable.[14]

2. *Mutations are random in their occurrence, but evolutionary change is directed in its occurrence.* Individuals do not receive virtually identical sets of genes from their two parents, but slightly different versions of approximately one in ten of all genes. This means that if the environment changes, there is a considerable amount of variation available for selection, in other words, adaptive change does not have to wait for rare new mutations but can use existing variation. Examples of this are genes conferring resistance to insecticides in mosquitoes or tolerance to heavy metal pollution in grasses, which are present in low frequencies in most populations, and enable rapid response to new selection pressures if the environment changes.[15]

Furthermore there is a sense in which 'randomness', as used of a scientific event, is a confession of ignorance. Early statements that mutations are completely 'random' in their occurrence and effect have had to be considerably modified by a growing understanding of cell biology and

[14] B. Wallace (1956) 'Studies on irradiated populations of *Drosophila melanogaster*', *J. Genet.* 54, 280–293; R. J. Berry (1972) 'Genetical effects of radiation on populations', *Atomic Energy Rev.* 10, 67–100.

[15] R. J. Berry (1980) 'Genes, pollution, and monitoring', *Rapp. P.-v. Réun. Cons. int. Explor. Mer.* 179, 253–257.

chemistry so that the probability of a particular change in a gene can now be expressed fairly accurately.[16] However, randomness is a term which can be used only of events occurring in time. A Christian who accepts that God is both creator and sustainer of the world (Col. 1:16–17), but also outside the space-time fabric of it, must necessarily accept that he is in some sense in control of all mutational events.

For the ordinary man in the street, the apparent purposelessness of the raw materials of evolution is one of the most significant factors convincing him that there cannot be a God of order in control of the world, leading to the pessimism well expressed by Monod in his book *Chance and Necessity* (1970). In contrast, no committed Christian should be prepared to admit that even such a random event as a road accident is outside God's purposes for him or her. It is therefore especially important for the Christian to recognize and witness that there is no conflict in accepting a world which seems to be full of evidences of design and one in which functional adaptation derives from random mutation; we can assert the former by faith (Heb. 11:3), but for those able to understand, it is possible to strengthen and exercise faith by discovering more processes by which the world has come to be. In the words of the research scientists' text (which is carved on the door of the old Cavendish Laboratory in Cambridge) 'Great are the works of the Lord, *studied* by all who have pleasure in them' (Ps. 111:2).

3. *Natural selection is a process brought into being by God.* A common anti-evolution argument is that nature 'red in tooth and claw' is an effect of the fall. In fact this is a humanist argument against God, asserting that no loving God would create such a world as the one that we live in. Our reply is that the present situation is not as God originally intended it to be, but we have to be careful lest we imply that the evil in nature was therefore created by the devil. This cannot be so: the devil is not a creator. The order of the world is affected by the fall and the curse

[16] See, for example, C. Auerbach (1976) *Mutation Research* (London: Chapman and Hall).

of God, but God is still the creator and sustainer of all that is, and there is no lesser god or devil who is either a creator or upholder. It was God himself who subjected the creation to futility (Rom. 8:20). The processes we see in nature are God's processes, even if they are processes set up to deal with a fallen world rather than a perfect world. Natural selection is a divine institution in just the same way as the State is a divine institution, or as it was the Father's will for his Son to suffer (Lk. 22:42; 24:26. See also 1 Pet. 4:19, *etc.*). We assume God will work in a particular way; when he chooses another, we are surprised. Animals do eat one another, and we are even told lions seek their prey from God and God gives it to them (Ps. 104:21, 27).

We must face the fact that this is how the world is, and not try to escape by talking about an ideal world created at the beginning. Indeed, if we are to be honest, we know extremely little from Scripture about the biology of the pre-fall world, although one thing we do know is that plants and seeds were given to man for food, which means that those plants and seeds must have died in the biological sense. The 'death' introduced by the fall (Rom. 5:12) must be distinct from the death present before Adam's sin. This is acknowledged in no. 6 of the Opening Theses. We shall return to this point (pp. 101f.).

The fact of evolution

Although there have been arguments about the mechanism of change, few people deny that small or microevolutionary steps can take place (Thesis 11); any debate there is concerns the reality of larger or *macroevolutionary* changes. We must therefore ask whether there is any evidence that macroevolutionary changes have ever occurred, and if so, whether they can be explained by the same mechanism as that described above.

The evidence for macroevolution

Darwin himself was first convinced of the inadequacy of the idea that the world was created in a short space of time, and had not changed since, by observing geographical variation in living things. For example, he wrote from the Galapagos Islands,

> I never dreamed that islands, about 50 or 60 miles apart and most of them in sight of each other, formed of precisely the same rocks, rising to nearly equal height, would be differently tenanted; but ... I obtained sufficient materials to establish this most remarkable fact in the distribution of organic beings.

Morphological and physiological resemblance between putatively related forms is only limited evidence for evolution, since such resemblances can usually be explained by different hypotheses; the only certain evidence for the fact that evolution has occurred comes from fossils.

How good is the fossil evidence? Leaving aside speculations that the fossils represent previous creations destroyed by God (as suggested in Scofield's References) or that they are artefacts embedded by God in the rocks 'to confuse godless scientists', we must ask whether examples of long-continued changes are ever found in fossil strata. Anti-evolutionists claim that transitional forms between groups are consistently absent. For example, in *Evolution – the Fossils Say No!*, a book which has had a wide circulation in the USA, Gish has written,

> While transitions at the subspecies level are observable and some at the species level may be inferred, the absence of transitional forms between higher categories (the created kinds of the creation model) is regular and systematic.[17]

Sylvia Baker states bluntly:

> Apart from archaeopteryx (a primitive bird), nothing in the fossil record suggests a convincing link between animals of different types.[18]

These statements are wrong:
  a. Missing links do occur. This is a matter of fact,

---

[17] D. T. Gish (1978) *Evolution – The Fossils Say No!* (San Diego: Creation-Life).

[18] S. Baker (1976) *Bone of Contention* (Welwyn and Grand Rapids: Evangelical Press).

and reference to palaeontological literature will show that more are continually being discovered. However, an article by Cuffey[19] is worth quoting, because it was published in an evangelical journal as a specific contribution 'toward resolving the evolution controversy'. Cuffey lists (with references) several hundred transitional forms, including many 'crossing from one higher taxon into another'. He concludes:

> The paleontologic record displays numerous sequences of transitional fossils, oriented appropriately within the independently derivable geo-chronologic time framework, and morphologically and chronologically connecting earlier species with later species (often so different that the end-members are classified in different high-rank taxa). These sequences quite overwhelmingly support an evolutionary, rather than a *fiat*-creationist, view of the history of life. Consequently, after carefully considering the implications of the fossil record, we must conclude that that record represents the remains of gradually and continually evolving, ancestor-descendent lineages, uninterrupted by special creative acts, and producing successive different species which eventually become so divergent from the initial form that they constitute new major kinds of organisms.

b. An evolutionist would expect missing links to be rare. Notwithstanding the well-documented occurrence of many transitional forms, there is no denying the fact that they are rare. One reason for this is that they must have been present in far fewer numbers than both their ancestral and descendent forms. Another is that evolution proceeds at very different rates in different groups at different times. The key macroevolutionary event is speciation (see below), and it is now clear that this may be an extremely rapid process followed by a 'genetic revolution' (see below) when change can be very marked. In some ways, it is surprising that there are so many missing links known.

[19] R. J. Cuffey (1972) 'Paleontologic evidence and organic evolution', *J. Amer. sc. Affiliation* 24, 161, 167–174.

The mechanism of macroevolution

Macroevolution is impossible if new species are not formed, because by definition all members of an existing species are capable of interbreeding and thus pooling their characteristics. However a species may be divided (by time, physical or ecological barriers, and/or reproductively isolated), and then the only constraints on divergence are those of the availability of variation and organization of the genetic material. Put another way, any evolutionary adjustment must be based on a single pool of genes (that is, a species); divergence and diversity can only arise when that pool becomes two or more (that is, following speciation). Greenwood has expressed this formally:

> The term macroevolution is generally used to account for the origin of 'higher' categories, yet these higher categories are in effect only our attempts to reflect simultaneously both the increasing diversity and the relationships of organisms within an evolving phyletic lineage. A lineage must stem from a single species. Its further development and diversification will depend on speciation events. I would equate macroevolution with speciation. . . .[20]

In other words, as soon as separate species arise (*i.e.* groups unable to crossbreed successfully), there is the possibility of both long-term and large-scale changes. The key issue is, therefore, whether new species can ever come into being.

It is impossible to know exactly what happened in past evolutionary events − as, for example, when the arthropods separated from the annelids or the flowering plants from the gymnosperms. However, there is no problem about accepting the possibility of these changes, *if* there has been sufficient time for them (and the age of the earth is discussed in this volume by Arthur Fraser), and *if* new species may be formed from existing ones.

It has often been said that the one topic that Darwin did not deal with in the *Origin of Species* was the origin

[20] P. H. Greenwood (1979) 'Macroevolution − myth or reality?', *Biol. J. Linn. Soc.* 12, 293–304.

of species. There has been a tendency to assume that this means that, even now, nothing is known about the process. This is not true. Addition of chromosome sets (polyploidy) producing sterility when crossed with the parent stock has been known for a long time to be a major factor in plant speciation. However, our knowledge of molecular mechanisms in biology (especially the way in which genes function and the role of gene duplication), and of the factors controlling variation in natural populations have only recently reached the stage where experimental study of the speciation process can sensibly take place. Speciation actually in progress has now been investigated in many cases, notable examples being that of Hawaiian *Diptera*[21] and Lake Victoria cichlid fishes.[22] Moreover, improved techniques of studying chromosomes have permitted new insights into cytological differentiation and its correlation with changes in the genes themselves.[23]

Our current knowledge of speciation is an excellent example of how science advances. We have already noted that missing links are relatively rare in fossil series. In fact a common feature in fossil-bearing strata is the persistence of a particular form for a long period without change, followed by its apparently abrupt replacement by a similar but distinct form, *i.e.* the sudden appearance of a new species.[24] This sequence, incidentally, is difficult to explain on a simple creationist model, even if extinction is allowed (Thesis 7). Hawaiian *Drosophila* exhibit today, in a living fauna, exactly the same characteristics of lack of variability and rapid formation of new species that palaeontologists recognize in fossils; *and* it has been possible to reconstruct the speciation process, and repeat it in the

[21] H. L. Carson (1978) 'Speciation and sexual selection in Hawaiian *Drosophila*', in *Ecological Genetics: The Interface*, edited by P. F. Brussard (New York: Springer-Verlag), pp. 93–107.

[22] P. H. Greenwood, *art. cit.*

[23] M. J. D. White (1978) *Modes of Speciation* (San Franciso: Freeman).

[24] S. J. Gould and N. Eldredge (1977) 'Punctuated equilibria: the tempo and mode of evolution reconsidered', *Paleobiology* 3, 115–151.

laboratory.[25] In other words, a genetical mechanism is known which explains the occurrence of the very different evolutionary rates observed by palaeontologists. Indeed it would be surprising to a geneticist if all speciation was slow and gradual, in the way that older textbooks caricature it.

These advances in our understanding of the nature of speciation do not mean that our previous lack of knowledge of the process was wrong in any moral sense, but merely that earlier ideas have been clarified or modified as information grows.[26] This is how science develops. But it must be emphasized that the overall effect of our better understanding of what goes on in nature has been to confirm the reality of the species as a discrete breeding unit and its role as the crucial element for (macro)evolutionary change. The modern biologist differs little in this from the biologists of the Victorian age; the difference is that we now know the mechanisms by which species can be formed.[27]

The extent of evolution

Microevolution is a fact; macroevolution is not, in the same sense. Darwin commented in the *Origin of Species* that the belief that all forms of life are descended from few or even one ancestor is argument by analogy, and 'analogy may be a deceitful guide'. New species certainly arise. Because of the virtual uniformity of the genetic code in all living things, evolutionists in general tend to assume that all forms of life are descended from a single origin – or, at most, two or three origins. Christian evolutionists have been divided on this point; some at least believe that a number of independent acts of special creation have

[25] E. Mayr (1954) 'Change of genetic environment and evolution', in *Evolution as a Process*, edited by J. Huxley, A. C. Hardy and E. B. Ford (London: Allen and Unwin), pp. 157–180; and A. R. Templeton (1980) 'The theory of speciation *via* the founder principle', *Genetics* **94**, 1011–1038.

[26] C. Patterson (1978) *Evolution* (London: Routledge and Kegan Paul).

[27] M. K. Hecht (1965) 'The role of natural selection and evolutionary rates in the origin of higher levels of organization', *Syst. Zool.* **14**, 301–317.

taken place, establishing the main groups of animals and plants. Rendle Short, for example, took this attitude in his influential *Modern Discovery and the Bible*. Some modern 'creationists' also come close to this view, interpreting the word translated 'kinds' (of animals and plants) as indicating major groups rather than species. However, there is no real evidence for this position. Unless there is clear biblical indication to the contrary, there is no particular reason to deny that most and possibly all forms of life have a common ancestor – and in Scripture we have the suggestion from the use of *bara* that God created biological life once only.

Man and evolution

The New Testament regards Adam as the first parent of the whole human race (Acts 17:26; Rom. 5:14ff.; 1 Cor. 15:45; *etc.*) (Thesis 5). Now the biologist puts man into a species he calls *Homo sapiens* which has been on earth for more than a million years, but it would be incompetent exegesis to regard the Bible's use of 'whole human race' as necessarily synonymous with the biological species *Homo sapiens*. This is clear as soon as we recognize that the essential features which distinguish man from the rest of creation are not anatomical or physiological traits, but God's in-breathing: in Genesis 2:7 we read that God took material that was already present on the earth, and made it a 'living man', literally a man-soul; while in Genesis 1:26–27 the characteristic of man is being made 'in God's image'. It is circular reasoning to argue that since we have two arms, two legs, two eyes, *etc.*, we are in God's image, and hence God must have a body like ours. The Bible says nothing of the sort, and implicitly condemns such anthropomorphism in the Ten Commandments; the Bible definition of God is that he 'is spirit' (Jn. 4:24). We are human because we have been created in God's image, not because of our membership of a species defined on morphological grounds as *Homo sapiens*; we are qualitatively separable from other hominids not because of any genetical event but because of God's in-breathing. It is in this respect that the relationship between a monkey and a man is completely different from that between a cat and a dog.

This distinction between the spiritual and biological nature of man is explicit in our evangelistic preaching. We emphasize that we become Christians not because of our upbringing or our parents, but only through God's sovereign grace (Jn. 1:13). If we assume that humanness consists of possessing certain physical or even mental traits, we are assuming something which is not in the Bible.

A Christian need have no problem with fossil man and discussions of the relationship of modern man with other hominids, because he is told that God *created* (a *bara*-event – see p. 80) man in existing material. There is clearly no difficulty in believing that God could have carried out this special creation in a hominid ape. There is no reason at all to believe that the hominid would change morphologically or genetically in any way that would be detectable to an anthropologist. The 'soul' does not have physical or genetic effects on our bodies (Jas. 2:18). On the other hand, the new man-soul had privileges and responsibilities in his relationship to God which are not immediately obvious to the biologist. We shall return to these later (p. 105).

This understanding of the creation of man raises three points:

1. *Who was Adam?* The New Testament is clear that Adam was a historical figure, as, for example, when Paul compares Adam with Christ (Rom. 5:12, 15). In his book, *Who Was Adam?*,[28] Victor Pearce has pointed out that Genesis describes Adam as a neolithic farmer (2:15) in the Middle East (2:8–14), and that urbanization and metalworking was already known during Adam's lifetime (4:17, 22). This suggests that Adam lived at a particular place on earth, ten to twenty thousand years ago after the final retreat of the Ice Age.

If Adam was created as recently as this, he could not have been the physical father of all human beings, since the Americas and Australia were already inhabited by man by this time. However, this is a problem only if we demand

[28] E. K. V. Pearce (1969) *Who Was Adam?* (Exeter: Paternoster).

that all men are genetically descended from Adam, and as we have seen, the essential part of God's creation of man was spiritual not physical. Humanness does not spread from generation to generation in the same way as physically inherited traits; every individual is uniquely endowed with spiritual life by God. Consequently it is quite possible that, at some time after God had created Adam, he then conferred his image on all members of the same biological species alive at the time. This is speculation, but it is in accord with Scripture, and solves such old chestnuts as where Cain's wife came from.

Notwithstanding, it is worth stating that there is no reason why a species should not be physically descended from a single pair, and it is possible that without any miracle Adam and Eve were the physical as well as spiritual ancestors of the human race. In this case, however, they must have lived at least 100,000 and probably nearer 200,000 years ago.

2. *There was a fall.* Just as acceptance of New Testament authority demands a historic Adam, so it demands a historic fall. The position of the evolutionist and anti-evolutionist is exactly the same on this: once we acknowledge that God created Adam for fellowship with himself and that man no longer is in fellowship with God unless he has accepted Christ's saving work for himself, it follows that there must have been a first occasion when man chose self rather than obedience, and fell. As Thesis 8 puts it:

> While we cannot be certain of the exact scientific or historical status of the animal and plant kinds described in Genesis 1 [and, we might add, the dialogue with the serpent in Genesis 3], the biblical account enables us to appreciate the creation and fall in concrete terms. No alternative ways of talking about them provide an adequate substitute. The biblical account cannot therefore be superseded, though it may be supplemented, by a scientific account.

3. *The fall was primarily spiritual in cause and effect.* Our first parents wilfully disobeyed God, and were excluded from his presence as a result. Subsequent attempts to live with God have brought a host of physical

consequences upon man. But it must be emphasized that these are secondary to the sin. For example, Adam was assured that 'the day you eat of [the tree of the knowledge of good and evil] you shall die' (Gn. 2:17), yet he lived on physically after the event in the Garden of Eden through which 'sin came into the world' (Rom. 5:12), and had many children (Gn. 5:4–5). This underlines the point already made (p. 93 and Thesis 6) that biological death was in the world before the fall; put another way, physical death and spiritual death are distinct, just as are physical life and everlasting life.

Again, Paul describes the so-called cosmic effects of the fall in Romans 8:18–24. This passage does not say that the fall automatically affected the whole of non-human creation. Paul's argument is that as long as man refuses to play the role God created him for, so long is the world of nature dislocated and frustrated. Since man is God's vicegerent on earth (which is part, at least, of the meaning of being 'in God's image'), he inevitably failed in his stewardship from the moment he first disobeyed God and dislocated their relationship.[29]

God could have created man *ex nihilo* at the time of the Garden of Eden, making him both body and soul at the same time. Such is the belief of Christian anti-evolutionists. The aim of this section has been to show that it is a belief not demanded by the Bible, and also that such a belief causes problems when man and other apes are compared. Man is genetically very similar indeed to the great apes.[30] There is no reason why God should not have made man with the same blood groups, inherited variations with similar frequencies, similar chromosomes, and – worst of all – anatomical anachronisms, as other mammals; but the Bible tells us only that God made man to be in his image and to have dominion over other living things. Our understanding of the humanness of man must

[29] C. F. D. Moule (1964) *Man and Nature in the New Testament* (London: Athlone Press).

[30] D. A. Miller (1977) 'Evolution of primate chromosomes', *Science*, N.Y. **198**, 1116–1124; E. J. Bruce and F. J. Ayala (1979) 'Phylogenetic relationships between man and the apes. Electrophoretic evidence', *Evolution* **33**, 1040–1056.

therefore depend upon our interpretation of these traits; it is consistent with our knowledge of God's use of natural processes to assume that he may have created them in the body of an ape which he had been preparing through the evolutionary process.

Inferences

Does it make any difference whether one 'believes' in evolution or not? Christians who do not, argue that evolution detracts from the sovereignty of God by insisting that the world and man could have come into existence by mechanisms understood by scientists, and without any need for divine intervention; and that it reduces the seriousness of the fall by inferring that man has 'risen' from animal ancestors and is getting better as he learns from his mistakes. They then leave the theological arena and question whether the palaeontological and anatomical evidence can buttress a conventional acceptance of large-scale evolution. On these grounds they claim that orthodox biology teaching brainwashes or indoctrinates students by presenting a biased picture of change and relationships, and hence is bad both from an educational and from a Christian point of view.

The fact is that the natural reading of the fossil evidence, other evidence for the age of the earth, and information we have about genetical mechanisms, all lead us to believe that the earth is very old and that creation has taken place over a long period of time. Most of the anti-evolutionists who have studied the evidence would have to agree, but then argue that the natural reading is not in fact correct because of the biblical evidence. Conversely, the theistic evolutionist must admit that the natural reading of Genesis 1 is of a creation that took place in six days of 24 hours, but then argue that other evidence makes it seem that the natural reading is not correct, and that Genesis 1 was not intended to teach us about the time-scale or mechanism of creation. He would argue further that Genesis 1 presents us with a way of thinking about creation which is wholly relevant today, and shows that it has an enormous number of things to teach us. Genesis 1 was not written in twentieth-century historical terms, and other passages that were taken for centuries in their natural sense now have to be understood in a non-literal sense (for example Psalm 93:1: 'The world . . . shall never be moved').

James Moore[31] has reviewed the Protestant struggle to come to terms with Darwinism in the nineteenth century. He concludes:

> Liberal Christians 'tended to forget Darwinism' because their theology was unable to receive it. Instead they were attracted to theories which could transform Darwinian evolution in accordance with their conceptions of the purposes and character of God. Those who concerned themselves with preserving historic deposits of truth . . . could say with T. H. Huxley: 'Not a solitary problem presents itself to the philosophical Theist at the present day, which has not existed from the time that philosophers began to think out the logical grounds and logical consequences of Theism'. *Those, on the other hand, who turned against established theological traditions, who took scant notice of historic doctrines of creation and providence, cut themselves off from Darwin's world and from the resources by which, if Darwinism were true, it could be kept a Christian world* [my italics].[32]

Belief in the authority of the Bible clearly transforms one's attitude to evolution, and in particular to man. The most common belief among non-Christians is that man is nothing more than the latest dominant species, due perhaps to be replaced in the future by another form. A humanistic development of this is the version of Julian Huxley, that man has reached the end of biological evolution and has now entered a phase of psycho-social evolution.

I believe that both a literalistic interpretation of the Bible and scientific humanism share the fallacy that a knowledge of evolutionary mechanisms necessarily

[31] J. R. Moore (1979) *The Post-Darwinian Controversies* (Cambridge: C.U.P.).
[32] *Ibid.*, p. 350.

excludes God.[33] As Thesis 3 says, 'If God chose to use processes to complete his creation, it was still his sovereign act. ... The events of nature represent God's sovereignty, whether they are subject to scientific explanation or not.' And as we have seen, 'there is no reason in principle to think of a sudden creative act as more God-like than a process'.

When we study Genesis 1, we are faced with a majestic description of God in action, but we are not told anything of the processes God used – 'God said ... and it was so.' This is fact, but it must not be read in the same way as a scientific narrative (Thesis 4). Similarly we are not told anything of the physiology or pathology of the rise and fall of Adam, but this need not affect our assessment of the historicity and continuing effects of the 'first Adam' as expounded in the New Testament. Indeed to suggest that Adam was a neolithic farmer living on the slopes of the Anatolian Plateau fairly soon after the last retreat of the Pleistocene Ice, who was 'in-breathed' by God and made a special creation enhances for many the reality of Adam[34] (Thesis 5). The important point is that Adam recognized and worshipped God, but rebelled against him with devastating consequences.

Adam and Eve died spiritually when they rebelled against God, but continued to live physically. We must distinguish between sin *per se*, which is a matter of our relationship with God, and its effects, which involve the abdication by man of his God-given responsibilities. The fall did not lead to physical death (Thesis 6) and we are wrong to infer that disease and suffering are necessarily and directly a result of sin – Christ himself pointed out that this was a misreading of Scripture (Lk. 13:1–4). Biological Adam can be studied by anthropologists and evolutionists; spiritual – that is truly human – Adam can be understood and studied only by believers (Heb. 11:3).

This brings us back to evolution. The study of the relationships, history and origins of living forms is a proper study for biological enquiry. It involves largely secular

[33] A. R. Peacocke (1979) *Creation and the World of Science* (Oxford: Clarendon Press).
[34] R. J. Berry (1975) *Adam and the Ape* (London: Falcon).

evidence and argument, and as with all scientific investigation, there are legitimate areas of dispute and obscurity.
Scripture gives no information or guidance about these
(Thesis 11). John Ray sought to see the wisdom of God
manifested in the works of creation. This is what any
believing scientist ought to aim for – but this does not
mean abjuring data from geology (Theses 7, 10) or
genetics, or any other discipline which can throw light on
'the work of thy fingers, the moon and the stars which
thou hast established; [and] man that thou art mindful of
him' (Ps. 8:3–4).

Evolution, in the sense proposed by Darwin and
modified (but not radically changed) by later knowledge
in the neo-Darwinian synthesis, is accepted by the vast
majority of biologists. An essay of this nature is not the
place to review fully the arguments that have convinced
generations of scientists, but I hope that I have said enough
to show that known genetical forces are sufficient to
explain the history of life. It is possible to deny that
Darwinian evolution has produced the world as we know
it because of some overriding preconception (such as a
particular interpretation of Scripture); it is intellectually
irresponsible to claim that it is impossible for biological
evolution to have been brought about by a mechanism
such as the one set forward in the *Origin of Species*.

The tragedy of the continuing 'creation' debate is that
it has obscured the glorious irony of the Darwinian revolution: Darwin brought God back into his world from his
exclusion 'out there' by eighteenth- and nineteenth-century
theologians. Nineteenth-century deism was inadequate;
only when God is seen to be both immanent and transcendent (which is what the Bible teaches, *e.g.* Eph. 4:6) will
Christianity become relevant once more. Science can speak
only of a mechanistic causality, while the Bible speaks of
a purposive one; the intellectual climate of modern man
makes a God active in his world necessary both scientifically and theologically.

It is worth emphasizing this. To many people, Christianity is not so much wrong as unnecessary. There is no
virtue believing in a First Cause who is impotent in the
world he created. But the evolutionary controversy has

forced us to recognize that any religion worth serious
consideration is one where the God is in constant control
of everyday events. Our God is so often too small – he is
One who has redeemed us and who is working his
purposes out, but One whom we do not like to recognize
in the events of everyday living. Consequently we profess
a desiccated and gutless Christianity utterly divorced from
that of the New Testament church, never mind that of
Luther, Cranmer, Simeon, Wesley, Booth, Moody and
Temple. Let us affirm: God has worked and is working
through normal, scientifically analysable events (as well as
through the miraculous supernatural); he is in control of
our body as well as our soul; we need fear no secular
discoveries because *true* faith is independent although
complementary to them. The Royal Society was founded
by men who wanted to know how God was working in
the world. May that be our attitude as well!

Conclusion

I have interpreted my task in this essay as being to
comment on the eleven Theses which were presented to
all the authors when we undertook to contribute in this
symposium. The first two are surely common ground; I
have referred to all the others, and hope thereby to have
confined myself to the real issues in the debate between
'creationists' and 'theistic evolutionists'. I am aware that
I have discussed some purely scientific questions, but this
has seemed necessary to clear up obscurities and miscon-
ceptions. My only concern in the debate is that God should
be seen to be sovereign and active in his world.

Frankly, I am bored and increasingly irritated by the
'creation debate'. I allowed myself to become involved in
it through counselling young people unable to make sense
of Bible teaching when faced with conventional evolution
teaching at school or college. Time after time, I find people
confused by pressure put on them to accept a particular
literalistic interpretation of Scripture which conflicts with
a convincing description (to them) of Darwinian evolution.
If this led to an obedience to scriptural authority, this
would be acceptable, but all too often I have found such

people questioning the whole of their faith. And it is so easy to show them from the Bible that there is no necessary conflict between evolution and God's creative work; that God can be seen to be in control of mutation, selection, differentiation, *etc.* in exactly the same way as he controls the circumstances of individuals.

When a Christian looks at the glories of God's world, his natural response is surely to give thanks for it – however much or little he knows about the processes that have brought it into being. I believe an evolutionist can share particularly fully in this praise, because he knows more about the wonderful intricacies of all he sees, and knows he is not seeing a static play-set but a series of forces interacting under God's sustaining majesty. A Christian evolutionist does not see the evolutionary procession as an automatic mechanism from which God is excluded: he sees a world upheld by its creator and made by him; and whether God uses entirely natural processes or intervenes occasionally or often does not matter to him. A Christian will not want to accept unscientific dogmatism from whatever source; he will be happy to discuss any weaknesses in neo-Darwinism, but equally to acknowledge God's sovereignty to use any methods he chooses in dealing with the world; he will repudiate the facile evolutionism which politicians, economists, psychologists and (let's face it) theologians have added to biology, but accept the biological theories of evolution for what they are worth. As Paul said, 'Have nothing to do with senseless controversies; you know that they breed quarrels' (2 Tim. 2:23).

Response to R.J. Berry

V. Wright

In his paper, Professor Berry writes as graciously and cogently as anyone espousing the evolutionary view could. Although Dr Berry may feel that evolutionists are willing to discuss the weakness of their position, this is not as apparent to onlookers as it is to him. One cannot help thinking of the furore created at the Natural History Museum when a suggestion of creationism was recently introduced into an exhibition. Such was the pressure from the evolutionary lobby that this was quickly altered. Indeed, Dr Berry confesses himself to be bored and irritated by the creation debate. That is unfortunate, since the debate is here to stay! Neither can the matter be swept under the carpet by his claim that Darwin brought God back into this world. Darwin and T. H. Huxley, as well as many modern evolutionists such as Julian Huxley and G. G. Simpson, state clearly their views that Darwinism was strictly a materialistic explanation which Huxley, for example, claimed eliminated the idea of God from rational discussion.

Evolutionary theory
It is difficult to justify the statement that 'evolution is as firmly based as astronomy or parasitology'. On the very definitions that Dr Berry gives I would be hard pressed to describe evolution as more than a model. I could hardly

use that term for astronomy or parasitology, which are much wider disciplines altogether.

Dr Berry says it is impossible to know exactly what happened in past evolutionary events, and then he goes on to say, 'there is no problem in accepting the possibility of these changes'. What, may we ask, happened to the 'science' of evolution? If we don't know what happened, but are reduced merely to believing the possibility of some process, do we call that science? We may feel that, in saying so, Dr Berry has surrendered his arguments, both for evolution as science and as fact, unless one may equate speculative possibilities with facts. Dr Berry enthusiastically embraces the neo-Darwinian or modern synthetic mechanism of evolution. He speaks as if it were a fact beyond dispute. May I remind him of the debate in evolutionary circles in the past few years? Gould states:

> If Mayr's characterisation of the synthetic theory is accurate, then that theory, as a general proposition, is effectively dead, despite its persistence as textbook orthodoxy.

Let us hope that we are not going to be exposed to much more of the dogmatism exemplified by Richard Leakey in his television series on the origin of man, when he had the extraordinary effrontery to declare, in the name of science, 'Evolution is no longer a theory; it is a fact.' Even *The Daily Telegraph* took exception to that!

Vestigial organs

It is interesting that not a word is written in Dr Berry's chapter about vestigial organs. This is not surprising, of course. Few biologists quote these as convincing evidence for the evolutionary model, since so many of these 'leaves not yet blown off the evolutionary tree' appear to have an important role in the body. All honour to the evolutionists that they no longer quote discredited evidence to bolster their case. Nevertheless, one is left with some disquieting thoughts. If it is so easy to leap from a part of the cliff that is crumbling, one wonders how firm is the rest of the ground on which they stand. Is it not likely that fresh waves of discovery will also erode some deceptively firm ground on which they now stand? Indeed, it is worrying to find a model so flexible that it changes with little difficulty to accommodate conflicting evidence. Such elasticity makes one question the strength and the substance of the view.

Speciation
It is apparent that within a species modification may take place by natural selection. The change in the peppered moth in relation to the Clean Air Act is an example with which most people are familiar. The deliberate selective breeding by farmers, and cruel counterparts in the dog world which produce bulldogs which can scarcely breathe, are other instances. What is not evident is that this process has operated in a wider realm. You cannot equate speciation with evolution. As even many evolutionists are pointing out, experiments involving flies in bottles, or peppered moths, in no way explain how flies became flies, moths became moths, tigers became tigers or people became people. These questions are often not asked by Darwinians, let alone answered. Increasingly, modern evolutionists are retreating from the position that natural selection plays a creative role in evolution.

The idea that such traits as resistance of insects to insecticides and the resistance of bacteria to antibiotics – and other examples cited by Dr Berry – have resulted from mutations, is purely the previous assumption of evolutionists. In fact, in some cases such as bacterial resistance to antibiotics, we know that this is not the case.

Palaeontology
It has been a strong point of creationist palaeontologists that in the fossil record intermediary forms are remarkably rare. Dr Berry suggests '. . . paleontological change tends to be gradual and progressive. . .'. In this he is out of touch with recent literature. Prominent evolutionists such as S. J. Gould, Niles Eldredge, Steven Stanley, Colin Patterson and David Raup are suggesting that there is little or no evidence for gradual change, and one certainly does not see progression in the fossil record..

Later Dr Berry states that transitional forms exist and

111

that more are being continually discovered. David Raup, after speaking of Darwin's dismay because he recognized that the fossil record was inimical to his theory, goes on to say that the record is actually worse today, since many examples of suggested transitions have been abandoned since Darwin's time.[1] In fact Raup speaks of the incompatibility of the fossil evidence and Darwin's theory because of the 'incompleteness' of the fossil record, which today is almost unmanageably rich.

An examination of Cuffey's list of 'several hundred transitional forms', which Dr Berry quotes, will expose the worthlessness of this evidence, much of which consists of speculations and some of examples since abandoned. Gish's book *Evolution – The Fossils Say No!* contains numerous statements by evolutionists who admit that the fossil record does not produce the evidence suggested by evolution. Readers should consider carefully the evidence cited in that book. An increasing number of modern evolutionists emphatically deny that the fossil record 'represents the remains of gradually and continually evolving, ancestor-descendant lineages. . .'.

If millions of species have gradually evolved through hundreds of millions of years, it can hardly be stated that evolutionists should expect that transitional forms should be rare. Environmental processes would act on transitional forms and terminal forms in exactly the same way. We have many millions of fossils of terminal forms and so we should have millions of fossils of transitional forms. Dr Berry suggests that transitional forms should be present in far fewer numbers than both ancestral and descendent forms. Does he not realize that in this statement he is denying the very evolutionary mechanism he so strongly advocates? He told us earlier that evolution proceeds by natural selection. What creatures are selected? The fittest are selected and thus survive to create subsequent populations. How is the fittest described? The fittest are those that reproduce in larger numbers. In fact, natural selection is differential reproduction. If the transitional form repro-

---

[1] D. M. Raup (1980) 'Conflicts Between Darwin and Paleontology', *Field Museum of Natural History Bulletin*, Vol. 50, p. 25.

duced in fewer numbers, they are by definition less fit and thus Berry's evolution becomes evolution of the unfit. The postulation of extremely rapid evolution is based solely on one fact – the absence of transitional forms. In fact, such a suggestion is contrary to all of genetics. The genetic apparatus of a creature is devoted to producing a similar creature.

However, Dr Berry does recant. Although with one breath he denies the rarity of intermediary forms, he says later, 'There is no denying the fact that they are rare.' You cannot have your cake and eat it! For those of us who are not palaeontologists, the remarkable shift in opinion on this score in the last year or two has been astounding. We are informed that the picture we have been given for the last decades of a gradual transition of animal and plant forms through the strata is not in accord with what has actually been discovered. What it really shows is that there are big jumps. Dr Berry, along with other colleagues, has modified the evolutionary theory to take this into account. What is alarming, however, is that for decades we should have been told authoritatively that the evidence points to this gradual transition, whereas now apparently this is not, and presumably never was, so. It is rather similar to the village clock striking thirteen – one distrusts all its previous pronouncements. Once you take the modern view that there may have been big leaps rather than gradual transition, we come close to a creationist position.

It merely leaves the question of time. I have discussed in my chapter possible explanations for the apparent age of things.

Authority

In many senses the debate comes down to a question of authority. Dr Berry's view is that the natural reading of Genesis 1 (and I would add, even more that of the fourth commandment) is a six-day creationist model. His natural reading of the scientific data is an evolutionary model. It then becomes a question of which of these banks of information we are going to take as the starting-point from which to scrutinize the other. He prefers to take his reading of the scientific data and mould the biblical text.

I prefer to take the natural reading of the biblical text and re-examine his scientific data. Let me add, however, that Dr Berry's repeated use of the phrase 'general scientific view' is prejudicial. This implies that evolutionary views are scientific and creationist views are non-scientific.

Because of Dr Berry's starting-point he runs into some heavy weather theologically. He feels it quite probable that at some time after God created Adam he then conferred his image on all members of the same biological species alive at that time. This is a flat contradiction of the biblical statement that Eve is the mother of all living humans. It also creates considerable problems with the self-evident biblical doctrine of original sin, particularly with the emphasis in the New Testament on sin entering by one man, and so death passing upon all men (*cf.* Rom. 5:12; 1 Cor. 15:21–22, 45f.).

Dr Berry takes the view that his interpretation solves such 'old chestnuts' as where Cain's wife came from. But to solve such questions, you do not need this view. Genesis 5, where we read Adam had sons *and daughters*, produces an obvious answer. I might take issue also with the exegesis of Luke 13, that disease and suffering are not necessarily and directly a result of sin. What the incident about the man born blind teaches is that his affliction was not the result of his or his parents' sin. There is every reason to believe that it was because he was bound up in the bundle of life with sinful humanity, and that disease and suffering are necessarily a result of the sin of the human race. In his opening discussion on the Hebrew word *bara*, Dr Berry suggests that, while this usually refers to a creative act, it may refer to a work taking place over centuries. However, later he uses the word to suggest that God created biological life once only, and, therefore, presumably he believes that in Genesis 1 the writer does refer to a creative act both in relation to life and to man. As Dr Berry says, 'We must beware lest our interpretation of Scripture is influenced by the secular norm.' If I may respectfully say so, the secular norm of today is an evolutionary model and an evolutionary philosophy. I would submit that this is precisely what Dr Berry has allowed to influence him.

No-one could deny that God *could* use an evolutionary process to bring into being the world as we know it today. The question we are discussing is: *Did* he do that? We are not discussing the interpretation of Scripture, but taking God at his word. It is all too easy to allow your views to be pressed into the mould of this world's thinking (*cf.* Rom. 12:2).

Conclusion

In most scientific debates where radically different views are propounded, the truth often lies in a synthesis. This is well seen in the arguments concerning the mechanism of lubrication of human joints, ranging from a fluid-film to a boundary regime. Both are most probably true, operating at different phases of the walking cycle. I suggest that the synthesis in this debate lies in 'evolution' on a micro-scale (within species) and creation on a macro-scale (God creating each species after his own kind, and in particular bringing man into being by a distinct creative act).

I leave the last word with the Decalogue (after all, God declared it directly): 'For in six days the LORD made heaven and earth, the sea, and all that is in them' (Ex. 20:11).

4
The origin of man

V. Wright

*Difficulties with the evolutionary model · The
uniqueness of man · Errors of the popular view of
science · How long did creation take? · Significance*

The present debate about origins is healthy. The assertion
that the evolutionary model is the only valid explanation
of the origin of man is being seriously questioned. The
extensive membership of the Creation Research Society in
the USA and the Newton Scientific Society in the UK
demonstrates this. All the members are science graduates
who have come to the conclusion that the evolutionary
model is incorrect. Others, outside their ranks, have
expressed similar doubts. A recent article in the *Schools
Science Review* argued that our current teaching of
Darwinism is indoctrinatory.[1] The school textbook statement that 'It is impossible . . . without doing violence
to the evidence to do otherwise than accept the *fact* of
evolution'[2] makes many teachers cringe. Recently in
discussions Harper[3] has commented on this further:

> Quite apart from the stranglehold on the imagination
> – and I know from personal experience that even
> when intellectually prepared to consider alternative
> ideas, I personally find that a blocked imagination

[1] G. H. Harper (1977) 'Darwinism and indoctrination', *Schools
Science Review* 59, 258–268.

[2] A. G. Grove, G. E. Newell and J. D. Carthy (1961) *Animal Biology*,
6th edn (London: University Tutorial Press), p. 791.

[3] G. H. Harper (1979) 'Alternatives to evolutionism', *Schools Science
Review* 61, 15–27.

can be the greatest obstacle to the student faced with a supposed 'mass of evidence' in support of Darwinism. Even if the student queries the 'evidence' from one class of phenomena and thinks it is unconvincing, he is unlikely to feel free to cast off the whole theory because of the mass of evidence that he thinks still resides in other areas of biology. It is surely up to us as teachers to prevent pupils and students getting into this situation; and in the present context, perhaps some 'positive discrimination' is needed to counteract the mass of indoctrinatory school text books, exam syllabi, children's readers, encyclopaedias, television programmes, etc., to which we shall still be subjected for some years at least.

It is frequently claimed that Darwinism is central to modern biology.[4] That may be so, but if all references to Darwinism suddenly disappeared, biological studies would proceed undiminished, and perhaps more fruitfully. Certainly in our own Research Unit the abandonment of the concept of vestigial structures has enabled us to investigate more purposefully the physiology of tissues in man for which no function was previously considered.

In the strictly scientific sense evolution is not a theory, in that we cannot repeat the experiment. That is why many prefer the term 'model'. Undoubtedly there is evidence consistent with this model. However, observations consistent with a theory do not constitute proof. For example, the increase of insanity in Great Britain was significantly correlated with the sale of radio licences, but no-one supposes that the two are causally connected. There are many other such spurious correlations; for example, the deaths by drowning were related to the number of ice-creams sold between 1951 and 1957, and the variation of the birth rate in Holland is related to the migratory habits of storks!

This chapter is mainly concerned with the origin of man. I suggest that the following considerations provide some of the strongest evidence to support the view that he is a special creation.

[4] M. J. Newman (1978) *Schools Science Review* 59, 766.

Difficulties with the evolutionary model

In the realm of *comparative anatomy* the upright posture of man has long puzzled advocates of the evolutionary model. The position of the acetabulum (hip socket) in relation to the animal's centre of gravity is very different in the quadruped and bipedal man. The progress from a four-leg to a two-leg stance would require relative movement of the acetabulum (Figure 1). If this was by small

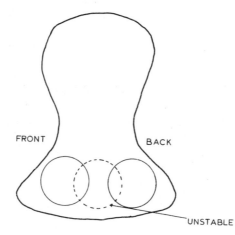

Figure 1. Diagram of lateral view of pelvis, showing the change in position of the hip socket required for change from a 4-legged to a 2-legged stance.

gradations an intermediate position would have been disadvantageous, and in terms of natural selection should have been eliminated. Again, the complexity of the eye and the difficulty of conceptualizing its development in evolutionary terms led Sylvia Baker[5] to change her views about origins. She comments:

> The turning point came one day at a seminar when we were discussing the evolution of the vertebrate eye. The eye is an extremely complex organ. It has the complicated system whereby light is directed to

[5] S. Baker (1976) *Bone of Contention* (Welwyn: Evangelical Press).

the back of the eye on to cells which are sensitive to it; it also has that even more intricate arrangement whereby the information then travels to the visual part of the brain so that we actually see something. We began at that seminar to discuss how this marvellous organ might have evolved. For an hour we argued round and round in circles. Its evolution was clearly impossible. All the specialized and complex cells that make up our eyes are supposed to have evolved because of advantageous mutations in some more simple cells that were there before. But what use is a hole in the front of the eye to allow light to pass through if there are no cells at the back of the eye to receive the light? What use is a lens forming an image if there is no nervous system to interpet that image? How could a visual nervous system have evolved before there was an eye to give it information? We discussed the problem from every possible angle, but in the end we had to admit that we had no idea how this might have happened. I then said that since we had found it impossible to describe how the eye could have evolved, the honest and scientific thing was to admit the possibility that it had *not* evolved. My words were followed by a shocked silence. The lecturer leading the seminar then said that he refused to enter into any controversy, while others in the group began to mock me for believing in God. I had not mentioned God! I had simply been trying to view the problem in an objective and scientific way.

In terms of *palaeontology* many reconstructions of 'primitive men' owe more to the preconceived ideas of the authors than to scientific observations. This has been reviewed in detail by Bowden,[6] whose assessment is less restrained than mine. He suggests downright dishonesty. It is well illustrated by Zinjanthropus. Figure 2 shows the same skull depicted in the *National Geographic Magazine* of September 1960, in a drawing by M. Wilson for Dr

[6] B. Bowden (1977) *Ape Men: Fact or Fallacy?* (Bromley: Sovereign Publications).

Figure 2. Zinjanthropus as depicted by three authors:
1. In *National Geographic Magazine*.
2. In British Museum.
3. In the *Sunday Times*.

K. P. Oakley, and in the *Sunday Times* of 5 April 1964. One author obviously thought he was dealing with a primitive man, another that the skull was akin to that of a gorilla. The different representations are largely due to the disposition of soft tissue and hair, of which the authors could know nothing, since these had long since rotted. Again, the coexistence of the footprints of brontosaurus and man in the Paluxy riverbed of Texas is difficult to explain on the evolutionary model.[7] The paucity of transitional forms despite decades of intense investigation does nothing to enhance the model, either.[8] Furthermore, extrapolation of population figures for men suggests his origin dates back to thousands of years, not millions.

Some of the most striking about-turns in evolutionary teaching have concerned *vestigial structures*. Many organs whose functions were unknown were regarded as 'leaves which had not blown off the evolutionary tree'. At one time the menisci of the knee were described as vestigial in man. These are the cartilages in the knee joint between the femur (thigh bone) and the tibia (shin bone), shown in Figure 3. Our own work shows that they carry 60–90% of the body's load in a walking cycle. The patients from

[7] A. E. Wilder-Smith (1970) *Man's Origin, Man's Destiny* (Wheaton: Harold Shaw).

[8] D. T. Gish (1973) *Evolution – The Fossils Say No!* 2nd edn (San Diego: Creation-Life).

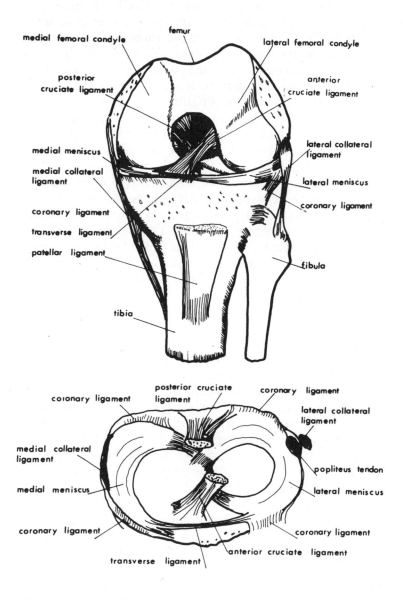

Figure 3. Menisci of the knee.

whom they have been removed are more likely to develop osteoarthritis. An even more vivid illustration is the thymus. In adult man it is often a shrivelled remnant, yet it is well developed in other animals. It was concluded, therefore, that it was a vestigial structure demonstrating the evolutionary origin of man. Yet one of the most dramatic advances in medicine in the last two decades is the discovery of its function. It now appears that for the foetus in the womb and in the days immediately after birth, this gland is crucial in developing the immunological mechanisms of the body. It enables the body's defences to distinguish between self and non-self. That is why our body rejects other people's tissues, be they heart or kidney, unless the body's reaction of rejection is suppressed. The dismissal of these tissues as vestigial was a reflection of ignorance. It may be argued that no advocate of evolution would cite these examples today. This, of course, is true, but once they were thought to be firm planks in the platform. In fact they have been shown to be rotten. We need to exercise a healthy caution before dismissing other tissues as vestigial.

The uniqueness of man

The Bible teaches that man is a special creation of God. Three times in Genesis 1 the Hebrew word *bara*, meaning specifically 'to create', is used. It occurs when God created the heavens and the earth, when he created living things, and a third time when he created man. This is fully consistent with the biology of man. He is distinct physically, mentally and spiritually. Apart from his upright posture, man's relatively large brain size is unique among animals, particularly the well-developed frontal lobes. Even more striking is man's uniqueness mentally. He alone of the animal creation can communicate in such a way that subsequent generations can build on that knowledge. Other animals can communicate, but not in this way. That is why man has technical development and the rest of the animal creation does not. This is related to speech and writing. Linguistic biologists have become increasingly interested in the origin of language. Professor J. C.

Marshall, in his book *New Horizons in Linguistics,*[9] states:

> The evolutionary hypothesis, as it related to language, far from being confirmed by recent research, is without empirical foundation. Language is radically different from all known forms of animal communication, and in spite of the vast accumulation of knowledge, scholars are still unable to propose a biological theory of language.

We may investigate the origin of language in two ways. First, we may look at the most ancient languages and ask if they are simple. The Sumerian script is the oldest. It is remarkably complex. A second approach is to study the language of the most primitive people alive today. I have looked particularly at the Maimainde tribe of Indians in Brazil. Their language is tonal (falling, rising, low, high); the vowels are laryngealized, nasalized, long; it uses implosive b's and a's, glottalized consonants, syllabic n's. It is certainly not simple.

Evidence such as this caused J. Lyons[10] to say,

> All the evidence so far accumulated by linguists confirms the view that . . . there is no group of human beings, in existence at present or known to have existed in the past, which does not possess a 'fully developed' language.

This conclusion harmonizes best with the view that man was a special creation, who came into being by a distinctive act of God.

Thirdly, man alone is a worshipping being, and the phenomenon is universal. You may hack your way through the densest jungle; you may come upon a tribe untouched by civilization, and you can guarantee it will be a worshipping community. The worship may be hideously distorted, even as it is brutally suppressed in some countries, but it is there. The most logical explanation is that

[9] J. C. Marshall (1970) in *New Horizons in Linguistics* (Harmondsworth: Penguin Books), pp. 229–241.

[10] J. Lyons (1970) in *New Horizons in Linguistics* (Harmondsworth: Penguin Books), p. 10.

man is unique in having a spiritual dimension to his nature. The contributors to this volume are agreed that man was made in the image of God, and that to ignore this would be unutterable folly, dooming us to ultimate frustration and futility. The very uniqueness of that aspect is not well explained on the evolutionary model. To do so usually involves tortuous explanations.

Errors of the popular view of science

In the light of this convincing evidence, it might be asked, 'Where have we gone wrong in our thinking in this century?' The tragedy is that we have cloaked the scientist with the mantle of infallibility. The man in the street, if he wants to strengthen an argument, states, 'The scientist says.' This is based on two fallacies. The first is that scientists are free from prejudice. History does not substantiate this generalization. In my own field of medicine Lord Lister used antisepsis in surgery. His techniques were not praised; he was vilified by members of the medical profession. His views would never have gained ground had not his patients lived and those of his detractors died! Scientists are as prejudiced as the rest of humanity. Secondly, it overlooks the changing nature of science. A scientist can never arrive at certainties (Figure 4); he can only disprove his theories. The 'mistakes' of science are legion. In the context of the present discussion the Piltdown man was displayed to generations of wide-eyed 6th-formers in the British Museum, until the forgery was exposed in *The Times* of November 1953 and 1 July 1954. It may be argued that this was a fraud rather rare in science. However, the scientist may be fundamentally mistaken. The explosion of the atomic bomb, in accord with Einstein's theoretical deductions, $E=mc^2$ (where E is energy, m is mass and c is speed of light), caused the rephrasing of a basic scientific axiom: 'Matter can neither be created nor destroyed.' It was the destruction of mass that provided a weapon of undreamt ferocity. The concept of energy had to be introduced.

It cannot be emphasized too strongly that a scientist is bound by the limitation of his knowledge. Subsequent

Figure 4. Science is a changing subject!

discoveries may lead him to a conclusion that is diametric-
ally opposed to his present view. In the realm of creation
there are interesting examples that do not conform to
generally accepted scientific timetables. All my learned
colleagues who have contributed to this volume would
agree that the miracles of Jesus were performed instantaneously. Three great creative miracles that he performed
were the turning of the water into wine at Cana of Galilee,
the restoration of the withered arm of the man Jesus met
in the synagogue, and the production of the bread that
fed the five thousand. If he did not know who had

performed these feats, the scientist might well dismiss such events, saying that, if they did occur, prolonged time-scales would be required. He would be wrong – not culpably so, since he is restricted by his incomplete knowledge. These miracles are common ground to Christians, whatever their view of creation, but the implications – that commonly held time-scales may be widely astray – sometimes escape us. Indeed, the difference in scales may be between that of a long period and that which is momentary. These instances do not prove that this is what happened in creation but they demonstrate that what one would normally consider in terms of years may happen in seconds. This leads to a discussion of times commonly quoted for creation.

How long did creation take?

Sincere Christians have differing views on this. Dr Scofield felt that each day of Genesis represented a long period. Dr Campbell Morgan believed that between the first two verses of Genesis there was a long gap. The phrase, 'Was without form and void', he said, could be rendered, 'Became without form and void'. Supporting evidence, it is suggested, is that Isaiah declared, 'God did not create chaos'. It could, of course, be argued that 'without form and void' and 'chaos' are not the same. The builder's yard with all the materials strewn around prior to constructing a skyscraper is without form and void, but it is not chaos, whatever casual observers may think. The building blocks are present for the creation.

For myself I believe in a six-day creation. A straightforward reading of Genesis by an intelligent man, not exposed to the evolutionary model, would suggest a literal six-day creation. The only way around this interpretation would be to suggest the account was allegorical or poetic. Neither in the opening chapters of Genesis nor elsewhere in the Bible is there a suggestion that the account is symbolic. Moreover, it is not found in the poetic section of the Old Testament. When the psalmist says, 'The mountains skipped like rams and the little hills like young sheep', he may denote a catastrophe or a time of rejoicing, depending on the context. It is poetic licence. In the historical section, however, we take statements at their face value. The account of creation occurs in the historical section. An even more convincing piece of evidence derives from the Ten Commandments. These were written directly by God and contain in the fourth commandment a clear reference to creation. 'Remember the sabbath day, to keep it holy . . . for in six days the Lord made heaven and earth, the sea, and all that in them is. . . .' With respect, it is worth reminding ourselves that it was the Creator himself who was speaking. The frequent assertion that God had to tailor his comments to the thinking of a given generation is difficult to sustain, since the Jews of the day, who are sometimes superciliously dismissed without any supporting evidence as 'primitive', could just as easily have understood a long period as they could a day.

Some may find difficulty in reconciling these clear statements with frequently quoted time-scales. It is important to appreciate that things may not be what they seem. We have already seen this in the creative miracles of Christ. May I introduce a further possibility? I introduce it for consideration, without dogmatism. The concept is that of 'contraction of time'. It is well recognized in science fiction that you may tumble out of a time capsule into another century. There is some biblical suggestion to support this phenomenon, associated with a curse. When Jesus went into Jerusalem he sighted a fig tree in full leaf. He anticipated it would be fruitful, but it was barren. He then cursed the fig tree, an event unique in his ministry. The next day the disciples observed the fig tree was dead, dried from the roots up. They were amazed because it was so soon withered away; a process that they would have expected to take weeks, occurred over hours. With the curse there was a contraction of time.

It would explain a good deal if at creation there had been a curse. In fact there was. When man rebelled against his creator, not only was his relationship with his maker severed, but God cursed the earth for man's sake. That was not trivial. It put the whole of creation in bondage, so that it groans as in the pains of childbirth right up to the present time (Rom. 8:22). And it will continue to do so, until Jesus Christ intervenes once more in the affairs of this world at his second coming. The restoration of a cursed creation is intimately connected with the ultimate redemption of man. From the time of the curse the earth began to produce thorns and thistles. There was a third occasion when the curse was associated with a contraction of time. At the cross (where, interestingly, men crowned the brow of Jesus with thorns: the fruit of their sin), Jesus was cursed of God as he bore the sin of the world. Jesus bore in hours punishment that it would take men eternity to pay.

How, it may be said, could this influence our dating methods? Figure 5a illustrates the principle of carbon dating, which is typical of many methods. A proportion of carbon dioxide (CO_2) in the atmosphere has radioactive carbon (C_{14}). While an organism is alive there is equilibrium between the amount of C_{14} in the atmosphere, which we know, and the animal or plant. Once the organism dies, there is no interchange with the atmosphere; the radioactivity decays. Since we know the rate of decay of C_{14}, we can deduce the age of a specimen from the amount of C_{14} in the atmosphere, the amount in the specimen and the decay curve. The calculations depend on two assumptions; firstly that the level in the atmosphere has remained constant, and secondly that the shape of the decay curve has remained unchanged (Figure 5b). Two catastrophes in the world's history (the fall and the flood) could have modified either of these, producing errors in our calculations.

Significance

These matters are not merely academic. It is important to appreciate the true nature of man. He has a spiritual dimension which we neglect at our peril. This is agreed by all contributors to this volume. However, the devil has a vested interest in discrediting the literal account of creation. It is only a step from disputing the face value of the facts of Genesis 1 to diluting the unpalatable truths of Genesis 3. The devil is anxious that man should be lulled into a sense of false security by casting doubt on the

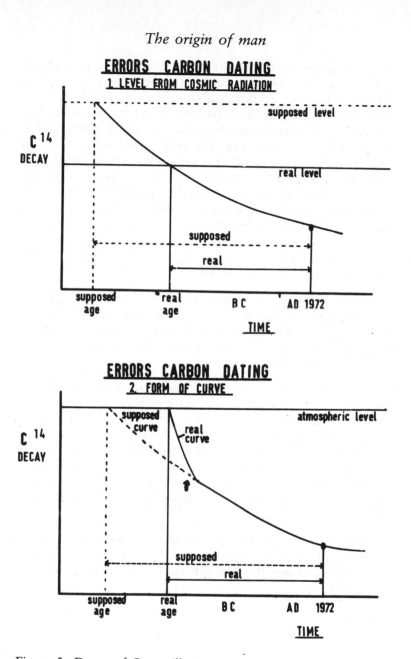

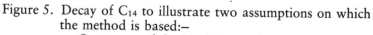

Figure 5. Decay of C_{14} to illustrate two assumptions on which the method is based:−
  a. Constancy of the level C_{14} in the atmosphere.
  b. Correct format of the rate of decay.

opening chapters of Genesis which contain the account of the fall. He would have us believe in the inevitable progress of man; that we are developing creatures. The Bible says that morally we are not; we are fallen beings. I am not suggesting that any contributor to this book holds such a view, but it is a fact that the churchmen most vocal in attacking the doctrine of original sin have been those who held the evolutionary model as the explanation of the origin and destiny of man. I would remind colleagues who would vehemently denounce such deductions, yet question the literal interpretation of Genesis 1, that a small breach in the dyke today becomes a raging torrent tomorrow. As Dr Oliver Barclay says in his analysis of the liberal evangelicalism of 1900 to 1910:

> If this little bit of history teaches us anything, it is that small concessions in basic doctrine can be devastating to the whole of our faith, practice and devotion. Even worship will not escape the anaemia of a doctrinal blood-letting.[11]

We cannot have a biblical view of sin without a literal Adam and Eve. That is why in the New Testament the guilt of man is intimately linked with his creation: 'As by one man sin entered into the world, and death by sin; and so death passed upon all men, for that all have sinned' (Rom. 5:12, AV). Furthermore, denial of the fall of man removes the need for redemption. Hence the New Testament also closely links the redemptive act of Christ with the creation of man.

> Therefore as by the offence of one judgment came upon all men to condemnation; even so by the righteousness of one the free gift came upon all men unto justification of life (Rom. 5:18).

11 O. R. Barclay (1980) 'Learning from History', *Christian Graduate* 33, 20–21.

Response to V. Wright

R. J. Berry

My immediate reaction to Professor Wright's chapter has been how little I disagree with the *facts* of his chapter, but how radically I disagree with many of his *interpretations* of the same facts: I dissent from his interpretation both of Scripture and of biological fact, and I comment on some of these in the next few pages. However, it is worth emphasizing that the argument between us (and by inference between any evangelical Christians who differ about evolution) is about interpretation; two devout believers may sit down before God's Word and the secular world, and understand them in different ways. I believe that my interpretations are right and Professor Wright's are wrong, but it would be foolish for either of us to deny that another meaning can be read into the facts in front of both of us. Indeed, there are a number of areas where Christians come to different conclusions from the same set of facts.

Dr Henry Morris has written that:

> One can be a Christian and an evolutionist just as one can be a Christian thief, or a Christian adulterer, or a Christian liar. It is absolutely impossible for those who profess to believe the Bible and to follow Christ to embrace evolutionism.[1]

[1] H. M. Morris (1980) *King of Creation* (San Diego: Christian Literature Press).

131

I strongly dissent from this judgment (except in so far as the term 'evolutionism' often implies a philosophy rather than a biological discipline), and the very existence of this book suggests that all the contributors (evolutionists and creationists alike) have been prepared to argue our case on the basis of Scripture, and Theses drawn from Scripture (p. 107). We are arguing about interpretations, not fundamentals.

The evidence for evolution

Professor Wright cites a number of morphological traits as contrary to his understanding of Darwinian evolution:

a. The human eye. Darwin himself in the *Origin of Species* commented,

> To suppose that the eye with all its inimitable contrivances for adjusting the focus to different distances, for admitting different amounts of light, and for the correction of spherical and chromatic aberration, could have been formed by natural selection, seems, I freely confess, absurd in the highest degree.

This is Professor Wright's conclusion also. However, Darwin then argues at length that function as well as form evolves; that optical sensors less 'perfect' than the eye as we know it, may nevertheless give advantage to their possessors; and also that the eye is not in fact 'perfect', but could theoretically be 'improved' (for example, for underwater vision). R. A. Fisher takes up exactly the same point, and adds his own quantitative insight, that:

> It was Darwin's chief contribution, not only to Biology but to the whole of natural science, to have brought to light a process by which contingencies *a priori* improbable, are given, in the process of time, an increasing probability, until it is their non-occurrence rather than their occurrence which becomes highly improbable.[2]

[2] R. A. Fisher (1954) 'Retrospect of the criticisms of the theory of natural selection', in *Evolution as a Process*, edited by J. Huxley, A. C. Hardy and E. B. Ford (London: Allen and Unwin), pp. 84–98.

Organs like the eye are certainly easier to explain for a 'creationist' rather than an evolutionist, but there is little difficulty in the latter accounting for them (*pace* the anecdote related by Professor Wright on pp. 118f.).

b. Man's upright posture. Wright supposes that, if man's 'progress from a four-legged to a two-legged stance ... was by small gradations, an intermediate position would be disadvantageous' (p. 118). However, all primates, with one or two possible exceptions, can *sit* upright; many can *stand* upright without support from their arms; and some can *walk* upright. The fact that only one out of the 189 species that make up the primates normally walks upright should not be surprising; in other words, the human upright posture is not so much a unique hominid possession but an expression of a definite trend among the primates. Furthermore, the erect posture results from a maintenance of foetal anatomy, along with many other human traits, supporting the suggestion that man, looked at purely physically, can be best described as a neotenous ape (that is, an individual in which sexual maturity occurs early; in man this seems to have been brought about by a slowing-down of developmental rates). Our species is pre-adapted to walking upright. Professor Wright falls into the common trap of seeking improbable transitional forms between ape and man, when there is no need to postulate them.

c. Vestigial organs. Professor Wright speaks of the gain in his own research when he abandoned the concept of vestigial organs. But he is merely behaving as a good scientist in this respect; science (like other intellectual activities) is littered with examples of difficulties that have arisen through clinging on to outworn ideas (*e.g.* phlogiston, the philosopher's stone, or the nature of light). In fact, 'vestigial organs' often illustrate the fact that function changes as well as structure (see above); these organs now have a function different to that in their ancestors.

d. Missing links. I have discussed these in my own essay. Suffice it to say here that:

1. They are much commoner than is allowed by anti-evolutionists.

2. On the modern genetical understanding of speciation they would be expected to be rare.

As far as geology in general is concerned, William Tanner, a senior American geologist, has written:

> The rock record, despite diligent search by many determined to find positive evidence of a brief earth history, has not revealed any such evidence. All of the evidence cited by them has been based on simple misreading of elementary facts. The so-called Precambrian human footprints of North Carolina (which I have examined and which are neither Precambrian nor footprints)[3], the supposed Cretaceous human fetus of Oklahoma (which is neither human nor a fetus), the reported Noachian deluge deposits of various places (which were neither simultaneous nor catastrophic): all of these are citations by persons who are willing to mis-state the observable and the verifiable facts of geology in order to support what they consider to be a biblical doctrine. . . . Geology *requires* a very long history, and the Bible *permits* a very long history. . . . The simplest best statement of fact concerning the creation controversy is: we do not yet know the final word, but the evidence points strongly in the direction of a torturously slow devel-

[3] Verna Wright refers to these or to something like them (p. 120). When I questioned Professor Tanner, he commented 'The tracks look like humans' footprints, and they constitute a trail. However:

A. The prints are fairly sharply defined, in a climate where tombstone inscriptions are commonly badly weathered after exposure for 100–150 years.

B. The individual prints have essentially an even depth at all points, whereas real human footprints are very poorly defined in the instep in comparison to the heel and toe, where the walking process produces indentations.

C. The measurements vary somewhat from print to print, requiring that the size of the foot changed from step to step.

D. The number of toes is not constant.

'It seems clear to me that we are dealing with carvings made by human beings, but not by human feet. They are probably a couple of centuries old, but I do not believe that they are as much as 1,000 years old. However, in no case are they as old as the rock, no matter what the actual age of the rock might be. Perhaps they are American Indian ceremonial carvings. . . . .'

opment, as God's purposes have been carried out according to the schedule of His choosing.[4]

One of the problems about morphological traits is that they can be explained in more than one way; they do not offer firm support either to evolutionists or to anti-evolutionists. As a matter of history, morphological data played very little part in the neo-Darwinian synthesis of the 1930s.[5] Clearly, if evolution has taken place, there must be signs of relationship between living forms. However biochemical data are much more convincing than morphological (*e.g.* DNA code, amino acid sequences of proteins, hormone structure and function, biochemical polymorphisms, chromosome structure, *etc.*); detailed comparisons between man and the other apes have been carried out for such characteristics.[6]

The interpretation of Scripture
By far the most important statement in Professor Wright's chapter is that 'the account of creation occurs in the historical section (of Genesis)', and he develops this assumption with relation to the 'days' of creation in Genesis 1. It is important to state unequivocally that there is no agreement that this is the correct way to interpret the creation narratives, even among firm Evangelicals. For example, Ellicott's conservative evangelical *Commentary* (1897) is explicit that

A creative day is not a period of twenty-four hours, but an *aeon*, or period of indefinite duration, as the Bible itself teaches us. . . . By the common consent of commentators, the seventh day, or day of God's rest, is that age in which we are now living. So in Zech. 14:7 the whole Gospel dispensation is called 'one day'; and constantly in Hebrew, as probably in all

[4] W. F. Tanner (1981) 'Time and the rock record', *J. Amer. sc. Affiliation* 33, 100–105.
[5] R. J. Berry (1982) *Neo-Darwinism* (London: Edward Arnold).
[6] See my essay, p. 100; also H. N. Seuanez (1979) *The Phylogeny of Human Chromosomes* (Berlin: Springer-Verlag); E. J. Bruce and F. J. Ayala (1979) 'Phylogenetic relationships between man and the apes. Electrophoretic evidence', *Evolution* 33, 1040–1056.

languages, *day* is used in a very indefinite manner, as for instance in Deut. 9:1.

J. A. Thompson in the *New Bible Dictionary* believes that 'the whole [of Gn. 1] is poetic and does not yield to close scientific correlations'. E. F. Kevan in the *New Bible Commentary* says:

> The biblical record of creation is . . . to be regarded as a picturesque narrative, affording a graphic representation of those things which could not be understood if described with the formal precision of science. It is in this pictorial style that the divine wisdom in the inspiration of the writing is so signally exhibited. Only a record presented in this way could have met the needs of all time.

Victor Pearce in *Who Was Adam?* (Paternoster, 1969) writes that 'the Bible story of creation is presented in picturesque portrayal of the goodness of God in His Creation and purpose in man'. James Houston in *I Believe in the Creator* (Hodder and Stoughton, 1979) concludes:

> It is a tragic mistake, when well-meaning Christians build up their views of creation solely on the grounds of scientific speculations or rebuttals to them, and overlook the fact that the doctrine of creation is a Christian doctrine about Christ, revealing the character of God as covenant maker with His creation.

Now my aim in these quotations is not to claim that Verna Wright is necessarily wrong in believing the creation narrative is literal history, but to point out that many conservative Evangelicals argue *from direct exegesis of Scripture* that Genesis 1 and 2 should not be read in this way. The antagonism of 'creationists' to evolution is rooted in their belief that the Bible excludes it; if the Bible does not exclude or conflict with evolution, the debate can be conducted in a much more open way without unnegotiable preconceptions.

Which leads me to the origin of man. Like Professor Wright I believe man is a special creation, distinct from animals and plants, because God 'created man in his own image' and because he 'breathed into his nostrils the breath of life'. I have described in my own essay how I interpret this: here I merely repeat that it surely means the essential part of our human-ness is our spiritual nature; to claim that we are *also* physically and mentally unique (as Wright does, p. 122), is unnecessary in Scripture, and contrary to the vast amount of data suggesting our genetic relationship to the apes.

Conclusions

'Creationists' (I refuse to use the term without inverted commas; like all Bible-believing Christians I too believe in God's initiative and control – indeed his entire sovereignty – over the whole of creation) read the natural world in the light of their interpretation of Scripture. People like me are regarded as brainwashed and confused by evolutionary dogma. Notwithstanding we all presumably agree that we should approach both the Bible and the natural world humbly, and seek the Spirit's help in interpreting them both. In my comments on Professors Wright's article I have tried to show that he *interprets* biological fact and scriptural narrative in a particular way; I *interpret* them differently. I suspect we shall have to agree to differ about our interpretations. But I hope I have said enough to demonstrate that neither of us can claim a monopoly of truth, and Christians who read these pages for a definitive 'answer' to evolution can only be urged to recognize that in the final analysis there can be no conflict between 'why' God created (which we find in the Bible: Heb. 11:3) and 'how' he created (which is an aim of science to discover). The sense in which I affirm that God is the creator and upholder of all things is not in any way weaker than Professor Wright's. We differ only about *how* he did it (and does it).

I understand that a major purpose of this volume was to identify the exact points of disagreement between Christian evolutionists and anti-evolutionists by discussing a series of Theses drawn from Scripture (p. 12). I discussed all the Theses in my own essay, and do not dissent from any of them (p. 107). It is not clear if Professor Wright has any reservations, because he does not explicitly mention any of the Theses. This is a pity: as an evolutionist, I am confident that my interpretations do not conflict with Scripture; it would have been helpful to learn whether the anti-evolutionists find any problems with the understanding of the Bible as expressed in the Theses.

5

A consistent biblical and scientific view of origins

D. T. Gish

Evolution theory versus probability · Evolution theory and the Second Law of Thermodynamics · Creation, evolution and the fossil record

The biblical doctrine of creation is of critical importance to the Christian faith. The very first verse of the Bible proclaims the fact of creation. The necessity for the redemptive act of Christ is based upon the fact that man was created without sin, in a state of perfection, with the inherent potential for life without death, and that he fell from this initial state through a voluntary act of wilful disobedience.

If man was not created through an act of special creation but rather has evolved slowly from some lower ape-like ancestor through mechanistic, naturalistic evolutionary processes, it is evident that he did not begin in a state of perfection. In fact, we should have every expectation that the man of the future will be nearer a state of perfection than he is today.

If man was not created perfect but has improved his condition greatly from an earlier animal stage, and is certain of future evolutionary improvements, why then is he in need of a redeemer? In fact, it is precisely this view that serves as the basis for the humanistic rejection of the cardinal Christian doctrine of the vicarious death of Christ on the cross of Calvary. The importance of the fact that man was created in the state described in the early chapters of Genesis cannot be overemphasized.

Let us briefly consider the account of creation in the first two chapters of Genesis. There is nothing in the context whatever to indicate that this account is to be considered poetical or allegorical. Specifically in the account of the creation of Eve (Gn. 2:21–22), we are told that God first caused a deep sleep to fall upon Adam. God then removed one of the ribs of Adam and used this for the creation of Eve. There is no question whatever about what the Bible says. There is no discussion necessary as to how a particular word is to be interpreted. What the Bible says is perfectly clear.

None of those who believe in evolution, atheist, theist or otherwise, believes this biblical account of the creation of Eve. It is rejected as a false account, for, they say, man and woman evolved together from some ape-like creature over a span of several million years. They simply do not *believe* the Scriptures at this point. However, the writers of the New Testament fully support the literal truth of this account of the creation of Eve. For example, in 1 Corinthians 11:8 we read 'For man was not made from woman, but woman from man' (see also 1 Tim. 2:13). Then when Paul is discussing one of the most critically important doctrines in the Bible – the literal bodily resurrection of Christ and of believers (1 Cor. 15) – we read, 'For as in Adam all die, so also in Christ shall all be made alive' (verse 22). From the construction 'For as . . . so also' it is clear that if all do not die in Adam, then none shall be made alive in Christ. If Adam is not a literal historical person, then the Christian has no hope of the resurrection. If Adam is merely figurative, then our resurrection is merely figurative.

The claim that God used evolution rather than special creation to bring the universe and the living things it contains into being denies the omniscience and omnipotence of God and makes a mockery of Scripture. According to the theory of evolution, ultimately all of evolution is due to mutations. No-one can rationally deny that mutations are random events. In fact, it is fair to say (and most evolutionists do say) that mutations are mistakes. They are equivalent to typographical errors. Furthermore, no rational scientist would deny that practically all mutations are harmful (in fact, it is difficult if not impossible to prove that any are beneficial). Many are indeed lethal.

Furthermore, the evolutionary process has apparently led to many dead ends. Evolution would certainly constitute the most wasteful, inefficient, cruel method God could have used to create. The concept of evolution is thus totally inconsistent with the attributes of God as revealed in Scripture.

The theory of evolution is an attempt to provide an entirely mechanistic, naturalistic explanation for the origin of the universe and all that it contains. The late Harlow Shapley of Harvard University said: 'In the beginning was the Word, it has been piously recorded, and I might venture that modern astrophysics suggest that the Word was hydrogen gas.'[1] Shapley went on to say that, starting with hydrogen and the natural laws and processes now operating, he could explain the origin of everything. Of course he could do no such thing, but his boast *is* the goal of those who maintain that the universe was created by a process of self-transformation beginning with a primordial chaotic state. No supernatural force or outside agency of any kind was involved or necessary, since a single act by a supernatural agency at any time during the process would frustrate all attempts to provide a naturalistic evolutionary explanation for origins.

A naturalistic, mechanistic origin of the universe would thus make a mockery of the Scriptures found, for example, in Romans 1:18–20, where we read:

> Now the holy anger of God is disclosed from Heaven against the godlessness and evil of those men who render truth dumb and inoperative by their wickedness. It is not that they do not know the truth about God; indeed he has made it quite plain to them. For since the beginning of the world the invisible attributes of God, e.g. his eternal power and divinity, have been plainly discernible through things which he has made and which are commonly seen and known, thus leaving these men without a rag of excuse (Rom.

[1] H. Shapley (1970) in *Adventures in Earth History*, edited by P. E. Cloud (San Franscisco: W. H. Freeman and Co.,), p. 78.

1:18–20, Phillips).

If God had merely endowed matter with certain properties which empowered this elementary matter to evolve into people, the theistic evolutionary process would be indistinguishable from a purely atheistic, mechanistic evolutionary process and there would be no way to discern the eternal power and deity of God or any of his other attributes through the things he has made. Rather than being 'without a rag of excuse', man would have every excuse for failing to recognize the divinity and the power of God in his creation. If matter was sufficient to do it all, then how can certain unseen attributes of God be plainly discernible through the things God has made? We conclude that the theory of evolution is incompatible with the Word of God.

All scientists agree that any process that involved or involves the intervention, in any way, of a supernatural being is not subject to the scientific method of observation, hypothesis and test. We must agree as scientists, then, that if the origin of life involved an act of God or required his influence or intervention in *any way*, the origin of life is obviously beyond the limits of scientific investigation. If God was the creator of life, the origin of life was miraculous in the most meaningful sense of the word.

There are therefore two views of the origin of life that are logically and philosophically consistent. Either life was created and its origin was miraculous and beyond the reach of the scientific method, or its origin was altogether naturalistic and mechanistic and therefore subject to rationalistic scenarios. It is contradictory and irrational to profess belief in God as the creator of life and at the same time to profess belief that life arose by a mechanistic, evolutionary process that is subject to investigation by the scientific method. It is, in fact, to want a creation in which nothing was created.

If it is historical fact that in the beginning God created all life, then the origin of life did involve his intervention. It was thus a supernatural process and cannot be accounted for by natural processes and natural laws now operating on planet earth. Those of us who believe that

God was the creator of life are thus confident that an analysis of proved principles of chemical thermodynamics and kinetics, well-established physical laws, probability considerations, and related scientific principles, along with our present knowledge of the incredibly complex, dynamic, intricately coordinated, self-maintaining, self-replicating entity we call the living cell, will demonstrate beyond a reasonable doubt that it could not have arisen spontaneously over *any* length of time by naturalistic, mechanistic processes due to properties inherent in matter. My own studies of this problem have convinced me that we are forced, by our present state of knowledge, to the conclusion that the origin of life by naturalistic processes can be dismissed with as much confidence as are schemes for the construction of perpetual motion machines.

Evolution theory versus probability

The modern theory of evolution, commonly known as the neo-Darwinian theory of evolution, is based on two basic assumptions. These are that all heritable variations may be ascribed to random or chance mutations, and that there is natural selection for fitness. The fittest, and thus those selected in a Darwinian sense, are defined as those that reproduce in larger numbers.

Ever since Darwin first put forth his theory, creation scientists have maintained that natural selection could at best be only a conservative force, weeding out the unfit; it would be powerless to generate increasing complexity and to originate something new or novel, and thus it would be powerless to change one kind of animal into another. They insist that at best such a process could produce only variants within an established kind and could never produce new and novel structures. Furthermore, *no* random process, genetic drift, mutations or otherwise, could produce millions of complex creatures from a single-celled organism in three billion years, or even in millions times three billion years. Even some who believe in evolution agree. Thus, Dr Murray Eden rejects the neo-Darwinian theory of random chance mutations with natural selection. He says:

143

It is our contention that if 'random' is given a serious and crucial interpretation from a probabilistic point of view, the randomness postulate is highly implausible and that an adequate scientific theory of evolution must await the discovery and elucidation of new natural laws – physical, physico-chemical and biological.[2]

Eden calculates that this assumed process could produce only relatively slight changes in three billion years and would, in fact, require billions of times longer to produce man and other complex species from a single-celled organism.

If natural selection is a relatively powerless force, then, by Sir Julian Huxley's own admission, evolution would be impossible. Huxley, referring to calculations of H. J. Muller, states that the chances of getting a horse from a single-celled organism by mutation but without natural selection is one chance out of $10^{3,000,000}$, a number so large it would take three large volumes of 500 pages each just to print[3]. Clearly, Huxley is saying that getting a horse by mutation but without natural selection would be flatly impossible. But, he declares, it has happened, thanks to natural selction!

Natural selection is evidently Huxley's god, for nothing less could convert an impossibility into a certainty. But, as Eden and other mathematicians have acknowledged, mutation with natural selection can work no miracles.

Evolution theory and the Second Law of Thermodynamics

Evolution theory contradicts one of the most firmly established laws known to science, the Second Law of Thermodynamics. The obvious contradiction between evolution and the Second Law of Thermodynamics becomes evident

---

[2] M. Eden (1967) in *Mathematical Challenges to the Neo-Darwinian Interpretation of Evolution*, edited by P. S. Moorhead and M. M. Kaplan (Philadelphia: Wistar Institute Press), p. 109.

[3] J. Huxley (1953) *Evolution in Action* (New York: The New American Library), pp. 45–46.

when we compare the definition of this Law with the definition of evolution by Sir Julian Huxley. The Second Law states that:

> There is a general natural tendency of all observed systems to go from order to disorder, reflecting dissipation of energy available for future transformations – the law of increasing entropy.[4]

> All real processes go with an increase of entropy. The entropy also measures the randomness, or lack of orderliness of the system: the greater the randomness, the greater the entropy.[5]

> Another way of stating the Second Law then is: 'The universe is constantly getting more disorderly!' Viewed that way, we can see the Second Law all about us. How difficult to maintain houses, and machinery, and our own bodies in perfect working order; how easy to let them deteriorate. In fact, all we have to do is nothing, and everything deteriorates, collapses, breaks down, wears out, all by itself – and that is what the Second Law is all about.[6]

Now compare these definitions or consequences of the Second Law of Thermodynamics to the theory of evolution as defined by Huxley:

> Evolution in the extended sense can be defined as a directional and essentially irreversible process occurring in time, which in its course gives rise to an increase of variety and an increasingly high level of organization in its products. Our present knowledge indeed forces us to the view that the whole of reality is evolution – a single process of self-transformation. [7]

There is a natural tendency, then, for all observed natural systems to go from order to disorder, towards increasing randomness. This is true throughout the entire

---

[4] R. B. Lindsay (1968) *Am. Sci.* **56**, 100.
[5] H. Blum (1955) *Am. Sci.* **43**, 595.
[6] I. Asimov, *Smithsonian Inst. J.*, June 1970, p. 6.
[7] J. Huxley (1955) in *What is Science?* edited by J. R. Newman (New York: Simon and Schuster), p. 278.

known universe; it is a natural law – the Second Law of Thermodynamics.

On the other hand, according to the general theory of evolution, as defined by Huxley, there is a general tendency of natural systems to go from disorder to order, towards an ever higher and higher level of complexity. This tendency supposedly operates in every corner of the universe, both at the micro and macro levels. As a consequence, it is believed, particles have evolved into people.

There is a basic contradiction between these two processes. Both cannot be true, but no modern scientist would dare to challenge the validity of the Second Law of Thermodynamics.

The usual, but exceedingly naive, answer given to this dilemma is that the Second Law of Thermodynamics applies only to closed systems. If the system is open to an external source of energy, it is asserted, complexity can be generated and maintained within the system at the expense of the energy supplied to it from the outside. Since our solar system is an open system, and energy is supplied to the earth from the sun, the decrease in entropy, or increase in order, on the earth during the evolutionary process has been more than compensated by the increase in entropy, or decrease in order, on the sun. The overall result has been a net decrease in order, so the Second Law of Thermodynamics has not been violated.

An open system and an adequate external source of energy are necessary *but not sufficient* conditions, however, for order to be generated and maintained, since raw undirected, uncontrolled energy is destructive, not constructive.

> The simple expenditure of energy is not sufficient to develop and maintain order. A bull in a china shop performs work, but he neither creates nor maintains organization. The work needed is *particular* work; it must follow specifications; it requires information on how to proceed.[8]

[8] G. G. Simpson and W. Beck (1965) *Life . . . An Introduction to Biology* (London: Harcourt, Brace and World), p. 466.

Thus a green plant, utilizing the highly complex photosynthetic system it possesses, can trap light energy from the sun and convert this light energy into chemical energy. A series of other complex systems within the green plant allows the utilization of that energy to build up complex molecules and systems from simple starting material. The green plant also possesses a system for directing, maintaining and replicating these complex energy conversion mechanisms. Without this direction, chaos would result and life would be impossible.

For complexity to be generated within a system, then, four conditions must be met:

1. The system must be an open system.
2. An adequate external energy source must be available.
3. The system must possess energy conversion mechanisms.
4. A control mechanism must exist within the system for directing, maintaining, and replicating these energy conversion mechanisms.

The seemingly irresolvable dilemma, from an evolutionary point of view is, how such complex energy conversion mechanisms and genetic systems arose in the *absence* of such systems, when there is a general natural tendency to go from order to disorder, a tendency so universal it can be stated as natural law – the Second Law of Thermodynamics. Simply stated, machines are required to build machines, and something, or somebody, must operate the machinery.

Another relevant argument involves the origin of the universe. In evolutionary theory, the universe is considered to be an *isolated* natural system, not requiring or utilizing any outside intervention or control. No energy entered the universe from an external source, and no work was performed on the universe by any system external to it.

According to the popular 'Big Bang' theory, some thousands of millions of years ago all of the energy and matter of the universe was crammed together in a huge 'cosmic egg'. That cosmic egg exploded and soon the universe

147

consisted of an expanding cloud of hydrogen and helium, which transformed itself into the incredibly complex and highly ordered universe we now have. Surely this postulated process would have involved a fantastic increase in order and complexity. A vast increase in information would have been required. When one compares the amount of information required to describe an expanding cloud of hydrogen and helium to the amount required to describe completely even a single bacterium, the contrast is obvious. Thus, Weisskopf has said:

> This evolutionary history of the world, from the 'big bang' to the present universe, is a series of gradual steps from the simple to the complicated, from the unordered to the organized, from the formless gas of elementary particles to the morphic atoms and molecules, and further to the still more structured liquids and solids, and finally to the sophisticated living organisms.[9]

Gamow has described this increase in order and complexity in the following way:

> We may also assume that in that distant past our universe was considerably less differentiated and complex than it is now and that the state of matter at that time could be accurately described by the classical concept of a 'primordial chaos' ... the problem of scientific cosmogony can be formulated as an attempt to reconstruct the evolutionary process which led from simplicity of the early days of creation to the present immense complexity of the universe around us.[10]

Thus, according to evolutionary postulates, the universe is an isolated system in which an enormous increase in order, complexity and information content spontaneously occurred. This is an undoubted violation of the Second Law of Thermodynamics. The evolutionist violates a basic premise of his model: that the origin of the universe can

[9] V. F. Weisskopf (1977) *Am. Sci.* 65, 409.
[10] G. Gamow (1955) *The Creation of the Universe* (New York: Viking Press), p. 20.

be explained completely on the basis of known natural laws and processes.

The creation scientist thus opposes the wholly unscientific evolutionary hypothesis that the natural universe, with all of its incredible complexity, was capable of generating itself, and maintains that there must exist, external to the natural universe, a creator, a supernatural agent, who was responsible for introducing, or creating, the high degree of order found within this natural universe. This view is extra-scientific, but not anti-scientific, as is the evolutionary hypothesis – which contradicts one of the best established laws of science.

Creation, evolution and the fossil record

The fossil record is hostile to evolution theory, something Darwin himself recognized, but, on the other hand, it is remarkably in accord with creation. Over a century after Darwin, during which the search for expected ancestors and transitional forms has been intense, the record is no better. In fact it is worse.

Raup, referring to Darwin's awareness that the actual fossil record was hostile to his theory, states:

> Well, we are now about 120 years after Darwin and the knowledge of the fossil record has been greatly expanded. We now have a quarter of a million fossil species but the situation hasn't changed much. The record of evolution is still surprisingly jerky and, ironically, we have even fewer examples of evolutionary transition than we had in Darwin's time. By this I mean that some of the classic cases of Darwinian change in the fossil record, such as the evolution of the horse in North America, have had to be discarded or modified as the result of more detailed information – what appeared to be a nice, simple progression when relatively few data were available, now appears to be much more complex and much less gradualistic.[11]

[11] D. M. Raup (1979) *Field Museum of Nat. Hist. Bull.* 50, 22.

The fossil record at its very outset contradicts predictions based on evolutionary theory. In Cambrian rocks are found billions and billions of fossils of highly complex forms of life. These include sponges, corals, jellyfish, worms, molluscs, crustaceans; in fact, every one of the major invertebrate forms of life have been found in Cambrian rocks. These animals were so highly complex that it is conservatively estimated that they required two to three billion years to evolve.

Numerous reports have appeared of the discovery of the fossils of alleged single-celled, microscopic, soft-bodied bacteria and algae in pre-Cambrian rocks (most geologists date the Cambrian period as beginning about 600 million years ago and stretching through 80–100 million years, while the pre-Cambrian Period refers to sedimentary rocks believed to be older than Cambrian).

If the complex invertebrates found in the Cambrian evolved from a single-celled ancestor, the record of the transition should be found in pre-Cambrian rocks, many of which are undisturbed and perfectly suitable for the preservation of fossils. Surely, if fossils of microscopic, single-celled, soft-bodied bacteria can be found, there should be no problem at all in finding fossils of transitional forms between these and the complex invertebrates of the Cambrian. Not a single transitional form, however, between single-celled organisms and the complex Cambrian animals has ever been found.

These facts are in full agreement with the predictions of the creation model. The fossil record *does* reveal a sudden appearance in great variety of highly complex forms with no evolutionary ancestors and *does* show the absence of transitional forms between the major taxonomic groups, just as postulated on the basis of creation. Thus, in a most emphatic manner, the known facts of the fossil record from the very outset support the predictions of the creation model, but unquestionably contradict the predictions of the evolution model.

The remainder of the history of life reveals a remarkable absence of the many transitional forms demanded by the theory. There is, in fact, a *systematic* deficiency of transitional forms between the higher categories, just as predicted by the creation model.

The idea that the vertebrates were derived from the invertebrates is purely an assumption that cannot be documented from the fossil record. On the basis of comparative anatomy and embryology of living forms, almost every invertebrate group has been proposed at one time or another as the ancestor of the vertebrates. The transition from invertebrate to vertebrate supposedly passed through a simple, chordate stage. Does the fossil record provide evidence for such a transition? Not at all. Ommaney has thus stated:

> How this earliest chordate stock evolved, what stages of developement it went through to eventually give rise to truly fish-like creatures, we do not know. Between the Cambrian, when it probably originated, and the Ordovician, when the first fossils of animals with really fish-like characteristics appeared, there is a gap of perhaps 100 million years which we will probably never be able to fill.[12]

One hundred million years of evolution and no fossilized transitional forms! All hypotheses combined, no matter how ingenious, could never pretend, on the basis of evolution theory, to account for a gap of such magnitude. Such facts, on the other hand, are in perfect accord with the predictions of the creation model.

The major classes of fishes are distinctly set apart with no transitional forms to connect them, as a survey of any book on vertebrate palaeontology will reveal. Errol White, an evolutionist and expert on fishes, in his presidential address on lungfishes to the Linnean Society of London, said:

> But whatever ideas authorities may have on the subject, the lungfishes, like every other major group of fishes that I know, have their origins firmly based in *nothing*. . . .[13]

The fossil record has thus produced neither ancestors

[12] F. D. Ommaney (1964) *The Fishes* (New York: Life Nature Library, Time-Life, Inc.), p. 60.
[13] E. White (1966) *Proc. Linn. Soc. London* 177, 8.

nor transitional forms for the major fish classes. Such hypothetical ancestors and the required transitional forms must, on the basis of the known record, be merely the products of speculation.

The transition from fish to amphibia is supposed to have required about 30 million years or so. Somewhere in the fossil record we should find transitional forms documenting the transition, for example, of fins into feet and legs. The fish that is supposed to have been the ancestor of amphibians, a crossopterygian fish, is marvellously designed for life in the water, with fins perfectly designed for balance, steering and locomotion in the water. The pelvic bones are small and loosely embedded in muscle, with no attachment with the vertebral column. None is needed. The fins do not support the weight of the body.

The oldest amphibian known, a labyrinthodont, has the basic amphibian limb, feet and legs. The pelvic bone is large and firmly anchored to the vertebral column. No-one has ever succeeded in finding a single intermediate form between the two. A large US natural history museum had a display on the transition from land to water on which was shown a remarkable transitional form between fish and amphibia – labelled 'Inferred Intermediate'!

Although, if evolution is true, museums should be overflowing with undoubted transitional forms, there are none. Consequently, a great fuss has been made over the alleged transition between reptiles and mammals. A close examination of this claim, however, considerably reduces its credibility.

The two most easily distinguishable osteological differences between reptiles and mammals, for example, have never been bridged by transitional forms. All mammals, living or fossil, have a single bone, the dentary, on each side of the lower jaw, and all mammals, living or fossil, have three auditory ossicles or ear bones, the malleus, incus and stapes. In some fossil reptiles the number and size of the bones of the lower jaw are reduced compared to living reptiles. Every reptile, living or fossil, however, has at least four bones in the lower jaw and only one auditory ossicle.

There are no transitional forms showing, for instance,

three or two jaw bones, or two ear bones. No-one has explained yet, for that matter, how the transitional form would have managed to chew while his jaw was being unhinged and re-articulated, or how he would hear while dragging two of his jaw bones up into his ear.

The origin of flight should provide an excellent test case for choosing between the evolution and creation models. Almost every structure in a non-flying animal would require modification for flight, and resultant transitional forms should be easily detectable in the fossil record. Furthermore, flight is supposed to have evolved four times separately and independently – in insects, birds, mammals (the bats), and in reptiles (the pterosaurs, now extinct). In each case the origin of flight is supposed to have required many millions of years, and almost innumerable transitional forms would have been involved in each case. *Yet not in a single case can anything even approaching a transitional series be produced.*

E. C. Olson, a geologist, in his book, *The Evolution of Life*,[14] states that, 'As far as flight is concerned, there are some very big gaps in the record' (p. 180). Concerning insects, Olson says, 'There is almost nothing to give any information about the history of the origin of flight in insects' (p. 180). Concerning flying reptiles: 'True flight is first recorded among reptiles by the pterosaurs in the Jurassic Period. Although the earliest of these were rather less specialized for flight than the later ones, *there is absolutely no sign of intermediate stages*' (p. 181). With reference to birds, Olson refers to *Archaeopteryx* as 'reptile-like' but says that in possession of feathers '*it shows itself to be a bird*' (p. 182). Finally, with reference to mammals, Olson states that, 'The first evidence of flight in mammals is in *fully developed* bats of the Eocene epoch' (p. 182). (My italics.)

Thus, in not a single instance concerning origin of flight can a transitional series be documented, and in only one case has a single intermediate form been suggested. In the latter case, the so-called intermediate is no real inter-

[14] E. C. Olson (1965) *The Evolution of Life* (New York: The New American Library).

mediate at all. As paleontologists acknowledge, *Archaeopteryx* was a true bird — it had wings, it was completely feathered, it *flew*. It was not a half-way bird, it *was* a bird.

The alleged reptile-like features of *Archaeopteryx* include claws on the leading edges of its wings, the possession of teeth, and vertebrae that extend out along the tail. It is believed to have been a poor flyer, with a small keel or sternum. While such features might be expected if birds had evolved from reptiles, in no sense of the word do they constitute proof that *Archaeopteryx* was an intermediate between reptile and bird. For example, there is a bird living today in South America, the hoatzin (*Opisthocomus hoatzin*), which in the juvenile stage possesses two claws. Furthermore, it is a poor flyer, with an astonishingly small keel.

The hoatzin is not the only living bird that possesses claws. The young of the touraco of Africa possesses claws and also is a poor flyer. The ostrich has three claws that are even more reptile-like than those of *Archaeopteryx*. No-one claims, of course, that the ostrich was an intermediate form between reptile and bird.

Recent articles have documented that *Archaeopteryx* had feathers identical to those of modern *flying* birds[15] and that there is nothing in the structure of the pectoral girdle of *Archaeopteryx* that would preclude its having been a powered flier.[16] Finally, it has been suggested[17] that the fossil of a modern type bird has been found in Upper Jurassic rocks, the same rocks in which *Archaeopteryx* is found. If confirmed, this would establish *Archaeopteryx* as a contemporary of modern birds and would thus preclude it as an ancestor.

With respect to claims for the reptile-mammal and the reptile-bird transitions, it would perhaps be relevant to note the comments of Ager, an ardent evolutionist, who said:

It must be significant that nearly all the evolutionary

[15] A. Feduccia and H. B. Tordoff (1979) *Science* 203, 1021.
[16] S. L. Olson and A. Feduccia (1979) *Nature* 278, 247.
[17] *Science News* (1977) 112, 198.

stories I learned as a student, from Trueman's *Ostrea/ Gryphea* to Carruther's *Zaphrentis delanouei*, have now been 'debunked'. Similarly, my own experience of more than twenty years looking for evolutionary lineages among the Mesozoic Brachiopoda has proved them equally elusive.[18]

Each generation debunks evolutionary stories, while generating evolutionary stories of its own that are eventually debunked by succeeding generations!

The fossil record of plants offers even less encouragement than does the fossil record of animals. For example, Darwin called the origin of flowering plants 'an abominable mystery'. In 1984, to evolutionists, the origin of flowering plants is still an abominable mystery! This dismal situation prompted Cambrian botanist E. J. H. Corner to write, 'Much evidence can be adduced in favour of the theory of evolution – from biology, biogeography, and paleontology, but I still think that to the unprejudiced, the fossil record of plants is in favour of special creation.'[19]

The fossil record of the primates, including man, is no better, in spite of a continuous stream of highly publicized and sensationalized statements emanating from certain physical anthropologists and the publication of highly imaginative intermediate links in textbooks and other publications.

Primates supposedly evolved from insectivores, such as tree-shrews. This hypothesis is not documented by fossils, but is based on inference from the study of living forms.[20] Furthermore, Campbell believes that a re-evaluation of the evidence shows that there is no close relationship between living tree-shrews and primates.[21] There is thus no evidence to link primates to shrews, either among fossil or living representatives.

The prosimians (lemurs, lorises and tarsiers are living

[18] D. Ager (1976) *Proc. Geol. Assoc.* 87, 131.

[19] E. J. H. Corner (1961) in *Contemporary Botanical Thought*, edited by A. M. MacLeod and L. S. Cobley (Chicago: Quadrangle Books), p. 97.

[20] A. J. Kelso (1974) *Physical Anthropology*, 2nd edn (New York: J. B. Lippincott), p. 142.

[21] C. B. G. Campbell (1966) *Science* 153, 436.

forms) are supposed to have been the first primates represented in the fossil record. Evolutionists believe that they evolved into monkeys, which later evolved into apes and men. Both the New World and the Old World monkeys, however, appear abruptly in the fossil record with no transitional forms linking them to the prosimians.[22] Apes also appear as apes with no links to either monkey or prosimian ancestors.

Evolutionary theory maintains that man's ancestry can be traced back to a common ancestor of ape and man. This hypothetical common ancestor has yet to turn up in the fossil record. The split occurred anywhere from four million years ago to nearly 30 million years ago, depending on who is telling the story. A number of suggestions have been made of intermediate species between ape and man, and in the past few years the series *Ramapithecus-Australopithecus-Homo habilis* (many anthropologists equate *Homo habilis* with *Australopithecus*)-*Homo erectus-Homo sapiens* has gained favour among evolutionary anthropologists.

For some years, based on a few fragments of jaws and teeth, Pilbeam and Simons championed *Ramapithecus* as a bipedal hominid[23] (all suggested links between ape and man are placed in the family Hominidae – the family of Man – and are called hominids). When more complete specimens of the jaws become available, however, reconstructions showed *Ramapithecus* to be nothing more than an ape.[24]

For many years *Australopithecus* has been suggested as a bipedal ape-like creature with dentition more human-like than that of modern apes, indicating that this creature was on its way to becoming man. Sensationalized reports followed Louis Leakey's discovery of a creature he called *Zinjanthropus* (East Africa Man), but after some years it was concluded that *Zinjanthropus* was the same as *Australopithecus*.

The commonly accepted view, or 'conventional wisdom', among anthropologists is indeed that *Australopithecus*

[22] A. J. Kelso, *op. cit.*, pp. 150–151.
[23] E. L. Simons and D. R. Pilbeam (1965) *Folia Primat.* 3, 81.
[24] A. Walker and P. Andrews (1973) *Nature* 244, 313.

was a bipedal creature with dentition somewhat like that of man, although some are beginning to quibble whether or not he was on the direct line leading to man. There have been some important dissenters to this conventional wisdom, however. These challenges have included those of Professor Lord Solly Zuckerman,[25,26] and one of his former students, Dr Charles Oxnard.[27–29]

For over fifteen years a research team headed by Lord Zuckerman studied the anatomical features of man, monkeys, apes and the australopithecine fossils. Practically all available important fossil fragments of *Australopithecus*, along with anatomical specimens from hundreds of monkeys, apes and humans were compared.

Writing about the claim by LeGros Clark and others that *Australopithecus* should be classified as a genus of the Hominidae (family of man) rather than as a genus of the anthropoid apes, Lord Zuckerman said:

> But I myself remain totally unpersuaded. Almost always when I have tried to check the anatomical claims on which the status of *Australopithecus* is based, I have ended in failure.[30]

Lord Zuckerman's conclusion is that *Australopithecus* was an ape, in no way related to the origin of man.

Oxnard's research led him to say:

> Although most studies emphasize the similarity of the australopithecines to modern man, and suggest, therefore, that these creatures were bipedal tool-makers at least one form of which (*Australopithecus africanus* – 'Homo habilis', 'Homo africanus') was almost directly ancestral to man, a series of multivariate statistical studies of various postcranial fragments suggests other conclusions.[31]

[25] S. Zuckerman (1966) *J. Roy. Col. Surg. Edinburgh* 11, 87.
[26] S. Zuckerman (1970) *Beyond the Ivory Tower* (New York: Taplinger Pub. Co.), pp. 75–94.
[27] C. E. Oxnard (1974) *U. of Chiacgo Mag.* Winter 1974, pp. 8–12.
[28] C. E. Oxnard (1975) *Nature* 258, 389–395.
[29] C. E. Oxnard (1979) *Am. Biol. Teacher* 41, 264–276.
[30] S. Zuckerman, *op. cit.* (ref. 26), p. 77.
[31] C. E. Oxnard, *op. cit.* (ref. 28), p. 389.

From his results Oxnard concluded that *Australopithecus* did not walk upright in human manner but probably had a mode of locomotion similar to that of the orang.[32]

In a more recent paper[33] Oxnard shows that in a particular orientation the pelvis of *Australopithecus* does indeed appear more similar to that of man than that of the ape, but when viewed in another orientation the pelvis of *Australopithecus* appears very unlike that of man but quite like that of the ape. He concluded that this creature probably had a hanging-climbing mode of locomotion, similar to that of the orang.

Oxnard's conclusions are that *Australopithecus* is not related to anything living today, man or ape, but was uniquely different. If Oxnard and Lord Zuckerman are correct, certainly *Australopithecus* was neither ancestral to man nor intermediate between ape and man.

Today Java Man (Eugene Dubois' *Pithecanthropus erectus*) and Peking Man (*Sinanthropus pekinensis*) are lumped together in a single species called *Homo erectus*. The specimen discovered by Dubois consisted of a skull cap, a femur (large leg bone) and three teeth, two of which eventually were shown to be from an orang and the other from modern man. Even to this day the evidence for bipedal locomotion of this creature rests on the femur found 50 feet from the skull cap, which Dubois had discovered a year earlier. Some anthropologists still doubt that the femur, which is essentially identical to that of modern man, belonged to the owner of the skull cap. Marcellin Boule, a famous anthropologist and evolutionist, said about Java Man:

> If we possessed only the skull and the teeth, we should say that we are dealing with beings, if not identical with, at least closely allied to the Anthropoids. If we had only the femora, we should declare we are dealing with Man.[34]

---

[32] C. E. Oxnard, *op. cit.* (ref. 29), pp. 273–274.
[33] C. E. Oxnard, *op. cit.* (ref. 29), p. 266.
[34] M. Boule and H. M. Valois (1957) *Fossil Men* (New York: The Dreyden Press), p. 123.

Fragments of about forty individuals have been found in a limestone cliff near Peking, China. Originally given the designation *Sinanthropus pekinensis*, this creature, as mentioned earlier, is now equated with Java Man and both are placed in a single species, *Homo erectus*. From the condition of the skulls, which apparently had been battered so the brains could be removed and eaten, and based on the fact that only skulls and jaws were found (practically nothing from the postcranial skeleton was discovered), it has been concluded that these creatures had been killed and eaten. The skulls and jaws had been preserved as trophies, evidently being carried to the site where they were found.

The story commonly accepted is that Peking Man was a cannibal and was thus both the hunter and the hunted. Marcellin Boule, after viewing the fossils and the tools found on the site, declared that he could not accept this idea.

In an article published in 1937 in *L'Anthropologie* (p. 21) Boule wrote:

> To this fantastic hypothesis [of Abbe Breuil and Fr. Teilhard de Chardin] that the owners of the monkey-like skulls were the authors of the large-scale industry, I take the liberty of preferring an opinion more in conformity with the conclusions from my studies, which is that the hunter (who battered the skulls) was a real man and that the cut stones, etc., were his handiwork.

There is thus very good evidence that the *Sinanthropus* creatures were the victims of hunters who were true Men. If this is so, then *Sinanthropus* could not have been the evolutionary ancestor of man, but must have been a large monkey-like or ape-like creature, in agreement with Dubois' final assessment of Java Man.

In more recent times Louis Leakey has reported findings that are astounding to those who believe in evolution. Leakey has found evidence for the contemporary existence of *Australopithecus*, *Homo habilis* and *Homo erectus* (the same as Java Man and Peking Man) in Bed II of the

Olduvai Gorge.[35,36] Even more startling is Leakey's report that he had found evidence for the existence of a circular stone habitation hut at the bottom of Bed I![37,38] Deliberate manufacture of shelters has long been presumed to be attributable only to *Homo sapiens*.

If *Australopithecus, Homo habilis* and *Homo erectus* were contemporaries, then how could one have been the evolutionary ancestor of the other? And how could either be ancestral to man, when man's artefacts are found at a lower stratigraphic level directly underneath the fossil remains of these creatures? These are very hard questions.

Neanderthal Man, long viewed as a primitive sub-human ancestor of man and at first designated *Homo neanderthalensis*, has now been elevated to the status of modern man, *Homo sapiens*. In more recent times it has been established that the skeleton on which the type Neanderthal had been based was of an arthritic old man. This was the only reason that he did not walk fully upright! Furthermore, X-rays of the bones and teeth of all of these individuals showed that they suffered severely from rickets, or vitamin D deficiency, which causes softening of the bones. It has also been suggested that they suffered from congenital syphilis. Thus, the so-called primitive features of Neanderthal Man were due to pathological conditions and were not genetically caused.

Lord Zuckerman apparently believes that, if man has evolved, he managed to do so without leaving a trace in the fossil record. He states:

> For example, no scientist could logically dispute the proposition that man, without having been involved in any act of divine creation, evolved from some ape-like creature in a very short space of time – speaking in geological terms – without leaving any fossil traces of the steps of the transformation.[39]

[35] M. D. Leakey (1971) *Olduvai Gorge*, Vol. 3 (Cambridge: C. U. P.), p. 272.

[36] A. J. Kelso (1970) *Physical Anthropology*, 1st edn (New York: J. B. Lippincott Co.), p. 221.   [37] A. J. Kelso, *ibid.*, p. 221.

[38] M. D. Leakey, *op. cit.* (ref. 35), p. 24.

[39] S. Zuckerman, *op. cit.* (ref. 26), p. 64.

In other words, if one excludes special creation as a possible explanation for man's origin, man must have evolved from an ape-like creature, but if he did, he did so without leaving a trace of that evolution in the fossil record. Thus the actual evidence accords fully with the concept of the direct special creation of man, but is contradictory to a supposed gradual evolutionary transformation through millions of years from some ape-like creature.

The discontinuities in the fossil record described above are not exceptions. The absence of transitional forms are systematic. All of the major types of plants and animals, which creationists believe to constitute the created kinds described in Genesis, are clearly set apart, both among living and fossil plants and animals.

Many palaeontologists since Darwin have been sufficiently candid to acknowledge this fact, although most refuse to give up their faith in Darwinism.

Richard B. Goldschmidt, in contrast to the majority of evolutionists, accepted the discontinuities in the fossil record at face value. He rejected the neo-Darwinian interpretation of evolution (the modern synthesis in today's terms), which is accepted by most evolutionists, at least among those who accept any theory concerning mechanisms at all. The neo-Darwinian interpretation supposes that all evolutionary changes took place slowly and gradually via many thousands of slight changes. Goldschmidt instead proposed that major categories (phyla, classes, order, families) arose instantaneously by major saltations or systemic mutations.[40,41]

Goldschmidt termed his mechanism the 'hopeful monster' mechanism. He proposed, for instance, that at one time a reptile laid an egg and a bird was hatched from the egg! All major gaps in the fossil record were accounted for, according to Goldschmidt, by similar events – something laid an egg, and something else got born! Neo-Darwinists prefer to believe that Goldschmidt is the one who laid the egg, maintaining that there is not a shred of evidence to support his 'hopeful monster' mechanism.

[40] R. B. Goldschmidt (1940) *The Material Basis of Evolution* (New Haven: Yale U. Press).
[41] R. B. Goldschmidt (1952) *Am. Sci.* **40**, 84.

Goldschmidt insists just as strongly that there is no evidence for the postulated neo-Darwinian mechanism (major transformations by the accumulation of micro-mutations). Creationists agree with both the neo-Darwinian and Goldschmidt — there is no evidence for *either* type of evolution! Goldschmidt's publications do offer cogent arguments against the neo-Darwinian view of evolution, from both the field of genetics and the field of palaeontology.

No-one was more wholly committed to evolutionary philosophy than was Goldschmidt. If anybody wanted to find transitional forms, he did. But concerning the fossil record, Goldschmidt had this to say:

> The facts of greatest general importance are the following. When a new phylum, class, or order appears, there follows a quick, explosive (in terms of geological time) diversification so that practically all orders or families known appear suddenly and without any apparent transitions.[42]

Now, creationists ask, *what better description of the fossil record could one expect, based on the predictions of the creation model?* On the other hand, unless one accepts Goldschmidt's 'hopeful monster' mechanism of evolution, this description contradicts the most critical prediction of the evolution model — the presence in the fossil record of the intermediates demanded by the theory.

In a recent article, David B. Kitts said:

> Despite the bright promise that paleontology provides a means of 'seeing' evolution, it has presented some nasty difficulties for evolutionists, the most notorious of which is the presence of 'gaps' in the fossil record. Evolution requires intermediate forms between species and paleontology does not provide them. . . .[43]

Macbeth says flatly:

> *Darwinism has failed in practice.* The whole aim and

[42] R. B. Goldschmidt, *ibid.*, p. 97.
[43] D. B. Kitts (1974) *Evolution* 28, 467.

purpose of Darwinism is to show how modern forms descended from ancient forms, that is, to construct reliable phylogenies (genealogies or family trees). In this it has utterly failed.[44]

He then goes on to quote other authors to the effect that the phylogenies found in textbooks are based on unsupported assertions, imaginative literature, speculations and little more.

The major predictions of the creation model are:
1. The abrupt appearance of highly complex and diverse forms of life with no evidence of ancestral forms.
2. The sudden appearance of basic plant and animal kinds without evidence of transitional forms between these basic kinds.

The fossil record reveals:
1. The abrupt appearance of a great variety of highly complex forms of life. No evolutionary ancestors for these animals can be found anywhere on earth.
2. The sudden appearance of the higher categories of plants and animals with no evidence of transitional forms between these basic kinds.

The historical, or fossil, record thus provides excellent support for special creation, but contradicts the major predictions of evolution theory. In answer to the question, did evolution really occur, the fossils shout a resounding NO!

The refusal of the establishment within scientific and educational circles to consider creation as an alternative to evolution is thus based above all on the insistence upon a purely atheistic, materialistic and mechanistic explanation for origins, to the exclusion of an explanation based on theism.

After many years of intense study of the problem of origins from both a biblical and a scientific viewpoint, I am convinced that the facts of science declare special creation to be the only logical and rational explanation of origins. '*In the beginning God created . . .*' is still the most up-to-date statement that can be made about our origins!

[44] N. Macbeth (1976) *Am. Biol. Teacher* 38, 495.

Response to D.T. Gish

D. C. Burke

Dr Gish confuses a number of issues in his forthright attack on evolution. First, he misunderstands the attitude to the Bible of those with whom he debates. All the contributors to this book hold the reformed evangelical attitude to Scripture – that it is the supreme authority in all matters of faith and doctrine. It is therefore misleading, and mischievous, of Dr Gish to say that those who do not agree with him do not believe the Bible. No constructive debate is possible if Dr Gish and his colleagues assert that those who disagree with them are outside the evangelical tradition. Nor is it charitable to say, as some have done, that Christian evolutionists are in the same class as Christian thieves, adulterers and liars (*cf*. p. 131). Maligning the reputation and moral standing of one's Christian colleagues is explicitly forbidden in the New Testament!

The plain fact is that all who write in this volume have taken the Theses printed in the introduction as a common basis – it simply is not true that all theistic evolutionists 'reject as a false account' the account of the creation of Eve or believe that 'Adam is not a literal person'. Many of us believe in a historical first pair, Adam and Eve, and a historical fall, and at the same time hold that they could have been physically descended from animals, although spiritually unique in the image of God. Thus all who write believe the Bible and the question is, what does the Bible

164

mean by the account in Genesis 1; and Thesis 4 states this clearly.

The crucial question in this debate, and one which is very often not brought out, is how should Genesis 1 be interpreted? The chapter is internally consistent in its own right, but into what category does it fall – modern history, poetry, science, *etc.*? A similar problem arises over the book of Revelation – the interpretation of which has differed, but where no consensus view has emerged. However those who have tried to base any science on the book of Revelation, or to predict the date of Christ's return, have frequently been proved wrong.

A number of issues are common ground in Genesis 1. It is clearly an authoritative religious account of origins – written for men and women of all time to show that God is creator of all that we see. It clearly has a formal literary style – as does the book of Revelation – and all of us agree that it is a 'Why' account – concerned to show the meaning of God's creation. But in what sense is it to be understood? Is it a 'How' account – telling us how God did it – is it literal history? The literary form of the narrative, the similarity to such forms elsewhere in the Bible (*e.g.* the book of Revelation) and the Psalms where 'the hills clapping their hands' is clearly not meant to be taken literally, suggest to me, but do not prove, that it may not need to be a scientific account.

How are we to decide? I suggest, in the same way that we handle such problems elsewhere in the Bible: by using all the evidence available to us. Here I submit that the evidence available by the plain use of the senses is relevant, and makes a literal reading very unlikely, for it is likely that the world is very old, was not created in six days, and that all living creatures are related.

Second, Dr Gish confuses evolution – that is the idea that all living creatures are descendants of those living in the past – with the mechanism of evolution. He agrees that mutation followed by selection can give rise to small-scale changes, but doubts whether it can lead to large-scale changes. In this he is in the company of a number of scientists who are doubtful, not because they believe the Bible to be a scientific textbook as Dr Gish does, but

165

because the mutation/selection hypothesis does not explain all the evidence, as Dr Gish has pointed out. It is clear that he rejects mutation/selection as a mechanism for bringing about change, but it is not clear whether he rejects evolution in the sense of derivation of all living creatures from others. My view is that the Bible is consistent with such a process, and the Theses do make this very point. However, Dr Gish is also confused about seeing any mechanism involving chance as being without any overall purpose or being inconsistent with God's control of this world. Radioactive material decays with a precise half-life (the time taken for the activity to fall to half its initial value), but there is no way of predicting which particular atom is going to decay next – it is purely random, although the overall result of such multiple chance events is precisely predictable. But neither the random event at the atomic level, nor the predictable event at the macro level, rules out a God who is in control of all this world's events – and whose regularity reflects his constant upholding power.

Third, Dr Gish maintains that 'if God was the creator of life, the origin of life was miraculous' and 'hence beyond the reach of scientific method'. But when life was created by God, as all contributors agree, then molecules were involved and something happened that was *describable*, although perhaps not wholly explicable in terms of physics and chemistry. Thus science does surely have something to say. It is misleading to oppose God's activity to the observations of science; the former are the basis of the latter. The birth of Christ (but not his conception) was a natural process. Was it not miraculous? Israel was 'created' as a nation by a *process* over centuries as described in the Bible. Was that also not miraculous?

Dr Gish also confuses several different ideas in his argument from thermodynamics. First of all, he asserts that the universe always tends towards disorder, so that evolution cannot be a natural process. This argument is false for two reasons; first, local order can arise even within a closed system as a consequence of the Second Law. For example, a crystal can form, and so order increase, at the expense of at least an equal amount of entropy being created elsewhere within the same enclosed system generally as a dissipation of heat. The origin of life might in this sense be compared to the formation of the crystal. Second, as Dr Gish admits, the earth is not a true closed system, and energy enters from outside (from the sun) and can be used to create order. This being the case, the proper question is: 'Can order arise naturally, at least for a lengthy time, in a non-equilibrium system?' Modern non-equilibrium thermodynamics clearly says 'Yes', and one might cite the example of the Red Spot of Jupiter, which exists constantly and changes little, but results from much more random swirlings in the atmosphere around it.

However, Dr Gish goes on to say that his argument is not strictly about thermodynamics at all; it is about design, without which life could not continue. Many Christians see evidence of God's design in the world around us, but this design does not have to arise from the direct manipulations of the designer. Life shows itself in its present form because of the outworking of the very constants of nature, set up long ago by God's choice, rather than by God's constant tinkering with the system. So an evolutionary process is not incompatible with God's design, while the origin of life could be a direct and necessary consequence of the way the world was set up in the first place.

Dr Gish has great fun in poking fun at some of the problems in the fossil records. He does less than justice to the huge body of evidence that palaeontology has assembled; the exact process by which one form changes to another is now a matter of considerable debate among scientists – debate triggered not by the criticism of the creationists but by the normal process of scientific enquiry. However, if the special creationists really want to supplant evolution they have to come up with a thoroughgoing explanation that deals adequately with all the scientific evidence and is consistent with their reading of Genesis 1. But they are not consistent – is the world just 6,000 years old, and was it created in seven 24-hour periods or not? Some special creationists are now talking of a world 10–20,000 years old with Day 1 much longer than the others. Others are involving special changes at certain times during the creative process in the viscous properties of rocks and water, rates of evaporation, crystallization and diffusion, thermal and electrical conductivity in order to produce the immense changes in the physical world assigned to Day 3.

These additions to the simple theory strike me as *ad hoc* additions to a theory that is beginning to lose credibility, and suggest that the seven 24-hour period creation cannot be held consistently. When exactly did the carnivorous habit, higher form parasitism and disease originate? After the fall and before the flood? If so, what happened before then? Was there any animal death, or disease, at all? Were the tigers vegetarian – and if so, why have we not found them? It seems to me that all the arguments Dr Gish makes against transitional forms can be made even more tellingly against such hypothetical creatures. Alternatively: did God create carnivorous tigers, parasites, animals prone to disease, as part of the initial creation? If so, why? Was Adam created from the dust by a process that was different in kind from that used to create you and me? Am I not formed from dust just as was Adam?

Finally, what was the nature of the curse – a spiritual blighting, as most have thought? Or an actual change in the structure, metabolism and habits of all living creatures, as the special creationists maintain? I find this effort to create a modern science on the basis of Genesis 1 wholly unconvincing – it does not lead to good science, but it also involves inconsistent attitudes to Genesis 1; looking for science where, in my view, none is intended, and distracting attention from the spiritual impact of the chapter.

6
Why some Christians believe in evolution

D. C. Burke

Introduction · How do sciences of the past work? · The evidence for an evolutionary process · Some difficulties of the 'young earth theory' · Some difficulties of the theory of evolution · Conclusion

Introduction

The term 'evolution' has been widely and often loosely used to describe changes in the detailed structure of proteins and nucleic acids, changes in biological form, changes in the structure of societies and changes in the values they hold ('the evolution of morals') and so on. By evolution, I mean the descent of living beings from distinctly different living beings in the past. This is what is often called 'descent with modification', and is the central tenet of the theory of evolution. It should be distinguished from the *mechanism* of evolution, whether that proposed by Darwin and Wallace (that of numberless small changes), or any other mechanism, also from the question of whether evolution has proceeded at a *uniform* slow rate, or whether there have been periods of rapid evolution and periods with little change, and also from the question of whether the *formation of new species* depends on the same mechanisms, as, for example, does the formation of different races of man from a single species.

Darwin said that species tend to become adapted to increasingly specialized environments; his ideas were not concerned with the notion of 'progress' at all. Yet because species were said to be 'better' adapted, then evolution

169

did become connected with 'progress' and 'betterness'. Biologists still refer to 'advanced' and 'primitive' species, and it became common to think that society, morals, *etc.* were improving (becoming better) and that this was an evolutionary, and therefore a natural, process. This idea has nothing to do with biology and is no longer widely believed; it will not be discussed in this article.

How do sciences of the past work?

Evolution is a science of the past, and like all sciences of the past it has special problems. This is because the events cannot be re-run, and therefore not all the usual methods by which other sciences work are applicable. Broadly, science is a technique for answering questions, and an experiment is merely a way of asking a single question – and getting an answer! Science asks 'How?' questions; it treats the world as a vast machine and attempts to find out how it works. There is no *a priori* reason to believe that it *is* a machine, and even less reason to believe that it is *nothing but* a machine; but it is a method that works – in that it provides us with information about the world which is useful – and perhaps, more important, information which is self-consistent.

Thus, although the scientific method rests on quite unproven and unprovable assumptions – that the world is real, that there is such a thing as a single, unifying explanation, that the world will continue to behave consistently – the fact is that it works. Historically these views rest on the way in which the Judaeo-Christian tradition has viewed the world, although not many scientists now working acknowledge the God behind the Judaeo-Christian tradition!

The end product of a scientific enquiry is a hypothesis that explains all the observations, and that is testable by new experiments. To put it more precisely, it has been argued by Popper that a scientific hypothesis should be 'falsifiable', that is, the planned experiment should have two possible outcomes – one that would be a consequence of the theory being true and one that would be a consequence of it being false. If it is not possible to 'falsify' a hypothesis – that is, if it is not possible to conceive of a scientific experiment that would show what would happen if the theory were not true, then, it is argued, the theory is not truly scientific.

No science of the past is falsifiable in that sense. The events of cosmology, geology and biological evolution cannot be re-run, so these theories cannot be demonstrated to be true in this way. Their validity must be tested in another way – by their ability to explain a wide range of observations. Theories of cosmology are able in this way to explain electromagnetic theory, the theory of relativity and Newton's law of gravitation. The theory of evolution is similarly wide-ranging, and we have to ask, 'Is it the most satisfactory and wide-ranging explanation of all the relevant facts?' In addition, theories of the past often make predictions that can be tested today. For example, evolution predicts that early man could not be contemporary with the dinosaurs; no cave drawings of dinosaurs are known, although there are drawings of other extinct animals (*e.g.* the mammoth) known, on scientific grounds, to be contemporary.

There is a wider sense in which all scientific laws are not necessarily true; for our theories explain only what we observe. The theories are not laws in the popular sense – they do not say what the world *has to do*. Thus any scientific theory may be replaced by one that describes the world more accurately; scientific laws are a series of approximations which we believe to be approaching the ultimate, true explanation. There is therefore a wholly healthy, continuing debate within the scientific community – a process of questioning, testing and restatement of our current scientific theories that is familiar to anyone who has worked in scientific research. Because this debate is so much a part of scientific advance, scientists distrust dogmatic statements about the world, for they cut short the process of scientific enquiry. Although it is easy to oversimplify the debate between the mediaeval church and Galileo, it is evident to many that the dogmatic statements made by the church about the nature of the world were derived largely from philosophical sources, were incorrect and held back our growth in understanding the world. It is therefore misleading to view the scientific community as one views a one-party State. There is of course often an accepted scientific view and there is also a scientific establishment, but it has often been wrong or only partially correct, and there is always vigorous debate within a healthy scientific discipline. There is also very considerable prestige to be gained as a reward for a new theory – a theory replacing Darwinian evolution would certainly be worth a Nobel prize! So debate goes on, about the theory of evolution as about anything else (see for example *Science* **210** (1980), 883–887); but as a scientist, I look for new theories to arise by the normal methods of science rather than by importing extra-scientific assertions from elsewhere. The latter process has too often proved to be misleading.

Scientists are aware, of course, that their work is not wholly free from imported values. The choice of fields in which to work, the approach that is used, the type of experiments that are carried out and even the way that they are interpreted, are all influenced by the values of our society. However the data of the experimental sciences still have to be explained, in as honest a way as possible, and it is the purpose of the remainder of this chapter to explain why the data lead the writer to evolutionary theory as the simplest explanation of the observed world. However I must not overstate my case. It is my view that the Christian has no particular stake in whether evolution is correct or not. The Bible in my view leaves entirely open the *method* of creation, and it does not tell us whether the theory of evolution is correct or not. Both are theories, both depend on analysis of evidence. What is the evidence?

The evidence for an evolutionary process

This comes from many different sources.

First, *variation* (that is, descent with modification on a small scale) *does take place now*. There is considerable variety of dogs, but they are all derived by selective breeding from a common stock. Man too shows considerable variation, and if we are all descended from Adam, considerable changes must have occurred – Adam could

172

not have been both black and white. The case of the peppered moth, in which the dark-coloured variety (whose darker colouring provides protection against a dark background) replaces the original light-coloured variety when the moth breeds in an industrial area, is a well-known example of such variation.

I do not think the evidence is disputed, but its significance is often overlooked. For the changes can be quite deep-seated involving mechanical changes (the Ainu of Hokkaido, Japan and other aborigines), while new species of dog can arise which cannot be interbred. Species are therefore very adaptable. Why should species be so adaptable if the world is only 6,000 years old and the environment has always been the same?

Second, *the method by which such variation occurs is, at least in some cases, selection*; either natural or artificial, acting on hereditary characteristics. This is certainly capable of bringing about small-scale variations (the case of Darwin's finches or the *Drosophila* species of the Hawaiian islands), and may be capable of bringing about much larger changes, given sufficient time. Whether these changes occur suddenly or gradually is at present disputed, but no-one doubts that such variation occurs.

Third, *the effects of geographical isolation*. Why is it that in areas which have been geographically cut off for longer, the fauna and flora differ to a greater degree? Australia and New Zealand have no native placental mammals but only marsupials and monotremes, while there are hardly any marsupials (the presumed ancestors of the placental mammals) alive anywhere else, where placental animals thrive. If Australia was cut off only at, or soon after, 4000 BC, this distribution is very odd, whereas an old world with the possibility of biological change provides a reasonable explanation – that marsupials gave rise to placental animals and, except in Australia and New Zealand, which were already geographically isolated by a big stretch of sea, the more successful placental mammals replaced the marsupials almost to extinction.

Fourth, *the earth appears to be very old*. The evidence is described elsewhere in this volume, but everyone agrees either that the world is very old, or alternatively that it appears to be very old. Therefore there is probably enough time for large-scale changes to occur.

Fifth, *fossils are found widely*. They have been studied in detail, and they obviously represent a huge variety of living creatures which are not found on the earth today. It is hard to convey the wealth of the fossil record to a non-biologist; a university degree in biology will only scratch the surface of this colossal collection. Huge numbers of very many types have been carefully collected and described by thousands of scientists over the last hundred years – and the criticisms made of evolution by religious writers often deal with a small proportion of the record. Clearly an attempt must be made to explain the fossil record; the key question is whether those fossils are related to each other and to living species, and if they are, what is the mechanism by which the related species change from and form to another. The different types could be quite unrelated to each other, each created by a separate creative act, or they could have all sprung from a single creative act, a single living form. Since all the writers in this book accept that God can work by process, as well as by scientifically inexplicable miracles, it does not seem to me that any theological case is at stake here. What is the evidence? Although the evidence has been overstated and overinterpreted, there is no question that there are fossil series where one can trace a relationship over a very long period of time.

The evolution of the horse family is a well-known example. The initial classification placed the fossils in a linear sequence, according to their geological age, to produce a series showing a gradual transition from a crea-ture about the size of a dog to the present-day horse. Further work showed that this was a considerable over-simplification and that there are at least six genera, some of which were living simultaneously but were biologically quite distinct, and that evolutionary change took place mainly in the New World rather than the Old World. The fossil record shows that a huge number of species, sometimes even whole classes, have become extinct, *e.g.* Tribolites, Graptolites, most big reptiles and amphibia, and some plant groups are known only as fossils. However, hardly any species, and no major groups, have become extinct over the last 2,000 years except by the hand of man. If the world is young, and every species survived the great flood in about 3500 BC, why has there been this immense change from instability to stability? To the writer the alternative explanation that the world is very old and the fossils reflect the response to a changing environment over a long period seems more likely. If organisms are really so responsive to change as breeding experiments suggest, it seems extraordinary that so many species became extinct over a mere 6,000 years. It is remarkable too that there are very few fossils of our present-day species except in the most recent strata. If the world were created recently and over a short period of time, surely fossils of present-day species should extend all the way back?

Sixth, *there is overwhelming evidence for the unity of all cellular processes.* This argues for a common, and single, origin for life – common ground for all Christians, both creationists and those that accept evolution. It is not only that there are obvious similarities between (say) all mammals, or all vertebrates, but that the cellular processes of all living creatures show an astonishing similarity. The way in which glucose is turned into energy is exactly the same in both bacteria and man – even though the process involves a long sequence of chemical reactions, controlled by a series of enzymes that bring out changes in an ordered fashion and in such a way that the maximum amount of energy is released. In turn, glucose levels in mammals are regulated by the hormone insulin, a substance which is structurally very similar over a wide variety of species. Indeed, the genetic code itself – the way in which the nucleotide sequence in the DNA of the genome is turned into the amino acid sequence of a protein – is common to all living organisms – with one minor exception described below. The modern discipline of biochemistry, the chemistry of living systems, can be taught almost without reference to the organism being used for study because of the unity of such processes. It is also common to study a single scientific problem – such as the determination of differentiation, in which one tries to understand how a single undifferentiated cell is directed into becoming a differentiated cell with more limited yet more complex functions – in a variety of organisms (frogs, the silk moth, the sea-urchin, slime moulds, to pick a specific example), because the answer that is emerging is common to all these species.

Within this wide-ranging unity, there is one major discontinuity – the distinction between the prokaryotes and eukaryotes. The former, comprising the bacteria and blue-green algae, show a number of deep-seated differences from the latter. These include the structure of the cell nucleus (prokaryotes have no defined nucleus), the presence or not of cytoplasmic organelles like mitochondria and chloroplasts (absent from the prokaryotes), the presence or not of a number of membraneous structures in the cytoplasm (the Golgi body), and the detailed mechanism of protein synthesis. There are a number of ways in which the prokaryotes resemble the mitochondria and chloroplasts of eukaryotes, and it has been suggested that these specialized cytoplasmic organelles arise by ingestion of prokaryotic bacteria into the cytoplasm of a eukaryote. Whether this is so or not, this discontinuity shows many of the features found elsewhere in the natural world – a difference imposed upon a basic similarity. This seems to me to be more readily explained by an evolutionary hypothesis – by suggesting that there was indeed a single type but that differences arose by genetic change and selection – than by a creationist hypothesis, in which the Creator uses two similar but distinct patterns. There is one other way in which all mitochondria differ from all other genetic systems – the genetic code is slightly different so that what is read as a stop signal elsewhere is read as an amino acid in mitochondria. This looks much more like an example of an evolutionary change arising by mutation, than a deliberate change in the normal procedure used by the Creator.

However, this approach can be pressed much further by determining the sequences of the proteins and nucleic acids of different species. Both molecules consist of long chains, rather like a necklace made up of twenty different coloured beads (the proteins) or four different coloured beads (the nucleic acids). A typical protein will have 150–650 of these beads (called amino acids) in a defined sequence – at each position in the chain the bead colour is always the same – and a typical gene will have 450–2,000 different beads (called nucleotides) in a similarly ordered sequence. It is obvious that there are many ways in which a 150 amino acid protein can be put together, but for a given protein from a given individual the sequence is always the same. There are sometimes small differences between individuals, but there are greater differences between different species. We know the amino acid sequences for many proteins from a wide variety of species, and when they are compared, several striking things emerge.

Let us look first at two species which show some obvious superficial similarities – humans and chimpanzees. Is there any similarity between the proteins of the human and the chimpanzee? They turn out to be astonishingly similar – a number of proteins have identical sequences (fibrinopeptides A and B, cytochrome C, lysozyme and several haemoglobins) and in a comparison of twenty proteins, it was found that there was less than 1% difference between the sequences of corresponding proteins of the two species. A similar result was obtained by comparison of 44 serum proteins by another method. I cannot overstress how unlikely it is that such a result is due to chance – the fact that the haemoglobin of man and the chimpanzee is identical is indeed remarkable. Two explanations suggest themselves – the first is that both species are descended from a common ancestor with a haemoglobin identical to that of man and the chimpanzee, and the second is that they are not related in any evolutionary way, but that each was separately created by God with a large number of identical molecules. Since the haemoglobin of man does not need to have exactly the same sequence as that of the chimpanzee to make it work, I think everyone would consider an evolutionary explanation the simplest way of explaining the facts.

Rather similar results are obtained by comparison of the nucleic acid sequences; these are more different from each other than are the protein sequences, and for two reasons. The first is that there is much more alteration in the nucleic acid sequences *between* the genes rather than inside them – that is, in regions that are not involved in determining protein sequences, and the second is that change is mainly in the third base of a codon (the group of a three nucleotides that determine, through the genetic code, which amino acid is selected) and since the third nucleotide in the codon can alter without altering the amino acid which is selected, the effect again is that the nucleic acid sequence is altered but the protein sequence is not. In other words change is possible, but often does not often take place if it would lead to change in function.

What happens when we compare amino acid sequences of more difficult species? There is much data but I will only discuss that for cytochrome C, a small protein (104 amino acids long) which plays an essential role in metabolism. The alterations in its amino acid sequence have been determined for a large number of species and are shown in Figure 1. The table shows that the more different any two species are, the more different are their cytochromes – and that is not too surprising. It also shows that there are similarities – the mammals are clearly more similar to each other than are the mammals to the birds or to the reptiles. But even simple yeast shows some similarities to higher animals! I think the suggestion that these differences arise by changes accompanying evolutionary change from a single ancestral form much the simplest explanation.

There is another way of using the amino acid sequences to find out how closely two organisms are related. If organisms are really related to each other in an evolutionary way, then the sequences also should be related – closer relatives showing fewer differences and vice versa. This comparison can be done with a computer, which compares the differences between different proteins, and then constructs a hypothetical ancestral sequence from which these similar sequences could have been derived. The ancestral sequences are compared in turn and a new ancestral sequence deduced, which in turn is compared with other sequences, both naturally occurring and deduced. This process produces an evolutionary tree, an example of which is shown in Fig. 2. Several approaches have been used which generate slightly different patterns, but the overall result is the same: a tree in which species are joined by lines which show how much structural relationship exists, while the length of the line shows how close or how distant is the relationship: the longer the line the more distant the relationship. The striking result is that such a method should give a result that is remarkably similar to the relationship arrived at by classical biological methods. Figure 2 shows the results of the computer operation, a tree produced *only* by comparison of the sequences of the protein cytochrome C. It shows all the mammals grouped together, separate from the birds, which are in turn separate from the reptiles. Yet these are all much more closely related to each other than they are to plants. The construction of these trees makes no assumption about biological relatedness – but produces an evolutionary picture similar to that derived from classical biology.

There is one more piece of information that these trees can provide; if the distances depict relatedness, and if it is assumed that there is a consistent rate of change in the amino acid sequences, then the distances are measures of the time taken for an evolutionary change to take place. The time should be measured in generations rather than in years, since what is important is any change in the DNA that is passed on to the next generation, and these changes must take place before production of the next generation. When this is done, the results indicate how long ago the two species diverged, and this can then be compared with the 'classical' dates derived from interpretation of the fossil record. The results show that different proteins seem to change at rather different rates, so that the method cannot be used as a precise 'molecular clock' to date evolutionary change, but it does give a picture that is broadly consistent with the picture emerging from the fossil record. That is, even though the absolute rate of change is not consistent, species which were distantly related on the evolutionary tree generated by the computer are a long time apart in the fossil record.

	Human	Monkey	Pig, bovine, sheep	Horse	Dog	Rabbit
Human	0					
Monkey	1	0				
Pig, bovine, sheep	10	9	0			
Horse	12	11	3	0		
Dog	11	10	3	6	0	
Rabbit	9	8	4	6	5	0
Kangaroo	10	11	6	7	7	6
Chicken, turkey	13	12	9	11	10	8
Duck	11	10	8	10	8	6
Rattlesnake	14	15	20	22	21	18
Turtle	15	14	9	11	9	9
Tuna	21	21	17	19	18	17
Moth	31	30	27	29	25	26
Neurospora	48	47	46	46	46	46
Candida	51	51	50	51	49	50
Yeast	45	45	45	46	45	45

Figure 1. Changes in the amino acid sequence of
shows the number of changes between the
those at the top of the table.

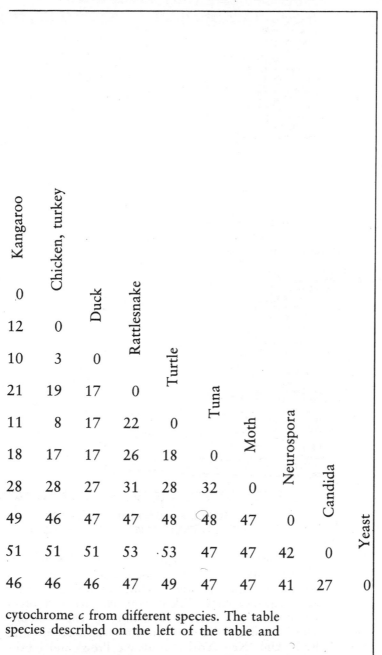

Kangaroo	Chicken, turkey	Duck	Rattlesnake	Turtle	Tuna	Moth	Neurospora	Candida	Yeast
0									
12	0								
10	3	0							
21	19	17	0						
11	8	17	22	0					
18	17	17	26	18	0				
28	28	27	31	28	32	0			
49	46	47	47	48	48	47	0		
51	51	51	53	53	47	47	42	0	
46	46	46	47	49	47	47	41	27	0

cytochrome *c* from different species. The table
species described on the left of the table and

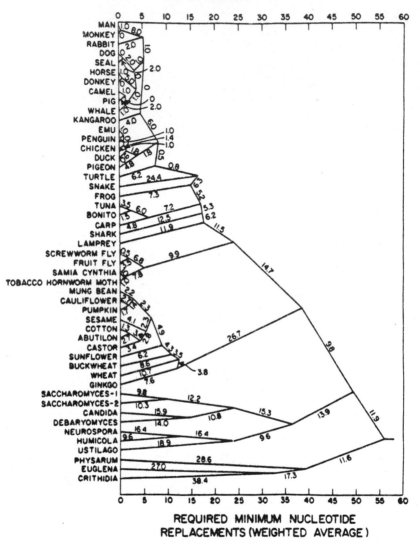

Figure 2. Phylogenetic tree of cytochrome *c* from 49 different species. The tree was constructed by the Fitch computer approach and exclusively utilized amino acid sequence data. Taken from chapter 1. Protein Evolution, by Russell F. Doolittle, in *The Proteins*, Third Edition, Volume 4, edited by H. Neurath and R. L. Hill (New York: Academic Press) and reproduced by permission of the publishers.

I do not want to overstate the precision of this method. What I find convincing is that organisms which have been thought to be closely related by using classical methods are found to have similar amino acid sequences; and the differences are completely consistent with an evolutionary relationship. It would have been so easy for the results of the two methods to be completely contradictory. They are not, and this strengthens my view that both are broadly correct.

Some difficulties of the 'young earth theory'

Many special creationists assert that their reason for adopting their position is that we must treat Genesis 1 literally as history in a more or less modern sense. Some make concessions on Day 1 being perhaps a long period, but even so, they are compelled by this principle to regard the land masses, the sun, moon and stars and all animals and plants as being created at about 4000 BC. If they modify this view, and make it 10,000 or 20,000 BC, they have abandoned their chief reason for their whole position. Thus, if the alternative view to an evolutionary view is a 'young earth' – and I think all special creationists hold some variety of this view – then there are two groups of scientific problems that I cannot myself resolve. Firstly, in almost every branch of science the universe does appear to be far older than 6,000 years. For example, we all hold the stars to be real, but the light that tells us that they are there in some cases must have taken millions of years to reach the earth. This has nothing to do with biological evolution or evolutionary philosophy, but we speak easily of stars being X light years away without realizing that that means that light has been travelling from them to us for X years, or we would not see them. Again, human archaeology has found civilizations that correspond closely to what we are told about Abraham in Ur of the Chaldees at about 3000 BC, but then when you dig deeper they appear to find civilizations going back far more than another thousand years. Or again, fossil remains of man *appear* to be much more than 6,000 years old, even if you totally discredit the claims of some recent discoveries to go back 3 million years. Again, some landscapes are very hard to explain except in terms of long-term erosion by ice (*e.g.* glacier moraines of bits of rock collected from far away), water (deep valleys in *hard* rock), wind or other very long-term erosion. The natural reading of the scientific evidence from a wide range of independent fields is most naturally explained in terms of great age, and in many of these fields it has nothing to do with biological evolution.

One possible answer to this is to say that the earth was created as a going concern, and therefore we do not see any evidence for recent sudden creation. Adam, for instance, on Day 1, must have seemed to be about 20 years old, trees 100 years old and rocks millions of years old. If you adopt this view, then there is no reason to expect any evidence of a young earth. We infer Adam's age from our experience of present-day processes, but the result is an illusion. But if that is what happened, why should it not have been consistently so throughout the universe? The whole universe may be only apparently old, and light that appears to have taken millions of years to reach us from the stars might have been created ninety-nine hundredths of the way here. Civilizations apparently older than 4000 BC may never have actually existed. This view can be held consistently, but it does not go with looking for evidence that the world is young. There is no reason to think we shall ever find any.

If you do not adopt the apparent age theory, then you must argue that the whole world was created about 4000 BC, or, allowing for some flexibility in Day 1, that the sun and moon, the sea and land masses and all animals and plants were created suddenly at about 4000 BC. We must then find evidence to support this view, and be able to explain the appearances of great age. The only adequate way to do this seems to be to adopt the 'flood geology' theory.

If flood geology could be established on a scientific basis, however, it would remove only one of the problems – the apparently great age of fossils and sedimentary rocks. It would not solve other geological problems, and it leaves those who hold it with a formidable array of problems. Were the carnivorous animals and parasites, which are often highly adapted to their roles, in existence before the fall? If so, why are there no traces of vegetarian tigers, and would they have been tigers at all? Did all the animals in existence really get into the ark, or was the great flood one that affected the whole of mankind, but not the whole globe? If the former is true, then did all the unique species from every island (*e.g.* New Zealand and the Galapagos Islands) make a miraculous migration, and did 1,000,000 beetles (there are over 500,000 species), other insects, parasites, whales and dolphins, really get into the ark? These are problems that do not arise if the flood is seen as a disaster of modest geographical scope, but concerning the whole of mankind and the animals with which man was concerned (mainly domestic). Even the New Testament talks of 'the whole world' when it means the Roman empire. My view is that acceptance of flood geology as a scientific theory, on a par with the theory of evolution, forces its holders into a series of increasingly unlikely scientific conclusions, and not surprisingly, perhaps, has convinced very few scientists. Surely Christians would be foolish to pin their faith to a *scientific* theory that is, at least, as vulnerable as the theory of evolution, and answers only some of the problems. If one's confidence in the Bible rests on flood geology, then, in my view, faith is on an extremely insecure foundation.

There does not, however, seem to be a third alternative. Either you accept the apparent age theory, or you accept flood geology. There is no point in accepting apparent age and also arguing that the appearances of apparent age are not there. I conclude that flood geology by itself does not seem adequate, and I observe that most of the flood geology writers (such as Messrs Whitcomb and Morris) have to accept apparent age up to a point in areas outside palaeontology; since their theory simply is not adequate by itself. None of us would put limits on what God can do, and it may be that there is a staggering series of miracles connected with the flood (though in no way hinted at in the Bible) and a staggering series of other miracles connected with a recent creation, all of which escape scientific detection; but it really is up to those who hold these views not only to criticize evolution but to produce a coherent and well-founded alternative. That I suggest has not yet been done.

As far as I can see, there is no strong argument either from general theology (it is as God-like to work through a long process as to work through a sudden creation) nor in any moral issue (God uses natural selection, as I think all are agreed, for small-scale changes), nor are these convincing scientific arguments against evolution in spite of the difficulties that it faces. The whole question hinges on the interpretation of Genesis 1. Many theistic evolutionists would accept that the Bible teaches a historical Adam and Eve and a historical fall. Genesis 2 and 3 can then be interpreted fairly literally though even the special creationists do not treat it entirely literally (*e.g.* Gn. 2:17 and 3:17 and 15). We need to ask, therefore, whether the special creationist view does follow necessarily from Genesis 1? Can we be sure that the days and kinds of Genesis 1 are meant to be taken as periods of 24 hours and species in the modern sense? The use of these words in the rest of the Bible does not convince me that that is at all necessary, though I can see why these terms are used as a timeless shorthand which does not mislead and emphasizes the sovereignty of God in the whole process of creation whether it was long or short.

Some difficulties of the theory of evolution

Very quickly after the publication of *The Origin of Species* in 1859, debate centred on the nature of man. Although Darwin himself had evaded the issue of the origin of man, the theological significance of the theory was quickly recognized. Man was, by implication, a near-ape modified by natural selection, and this seemed incompatible with the Bible's statement that man was created 'in the image of God' and with the capability of a special relationship with God. Was man no more than a 'naked ape'?

There are difficulties in applying Darwin's ideas to man; for a central point in his theory is the adaptation of a creature to its environment — yet man is remarkably unspecialized, able, even without modern technology, to live in a wide variety of climates. If man evolved by adaptation to an environment, what environment was it? The reverse appears to be true – that man has evolved to be more independent of his environment than any other species. Man differs too in his ability to communicate – for there is certainly a huge difference in degree from the higher apes, even if there is not a difference in kind. It has therefore been suggested that man's evolution is driven by his cultural rather than his genetic inheritance. That may be so, but it is not evolution in the accepted Darwinian sense. However there are certainly anatomical, physiological and biochemical similarities between man and the higher apes, and over the last few years many hominoid fossils have been found in East Africa. Their relationship to each other and to modern man is disputed, but it is possible that a plausible evolutionary relationship between them will ultimately be traced. Such a relationship has been used by non-Christians to argue against a Christian view, causing understandable reaction amongst Christians. The issues for Christians seem to me to turn upon whether Genesis 1 demands the creation of man directly from dust or via a process, and I see no reason to reject the second interpretation. Nor does the relationship seem to me to invalidate the objective nature of religious experience.

There are however two other difficulties with the evolutionary explanation – both concerned with the mechanism by which change is brought about. Darwin proposed that the changes were small and gradual, largely because he could conceive of no biological mechanism that would bring about large-scale changes and he did not want to involve divine intervention. It was therefore important to find the 'missing links' to establish the steady nature of the change. However change does not appear to occur as Darwin thought – some species do not change for millions of years (hence the phenomenon known as 'stasis'), while others change much more rapidly. The second difficulty is concerned with the emergence of new functions – what use would an eye be before it was an eye, if it was produced by a series of small changes? The honest answer to both these difficulties is that we do not really understand the mechanism of change. We do not know why new species appear suddenly after a long period of little change.

It has been argued by the creationists that since intermediate forms are not commonly found, the evolutionary argument for such a transition is weakened, and the creationist strengthened. This is not true; what we find in the fossil record is what was commonly present, and by definition those are the stable species. Whatever the transitional mechanisms, there would have been few transitional forms, and little to find in the fossil record if the changes were rapid. Nor do we understand the nature of changes that underlie the emergence of a new function. We do not even understand them when we can watch and study them, for example in embryonic development when organs appear from undifferentiated cells. It is therefore not too surprising that we do not understand how it could have taken place in the past. But to say 'God did it' is to miss the point; God is not just the answer to our unanswered scientific questions!

At present we do not know *how* such changes occur. A number of ideas have been tested and discarded. Darwin's original claim, that all organic variation could be accounted for by natural variation and selection, was replaced by the idea of mutation by alteration in DNA sequences and gene recombination. This is an excellent explanation of such inherited changes as albinism, but it is inadequate for our central problem. Currently the new discovery of transposable genetic elements has produced a more convincing explanation for large-scale genetic changes. We now know that certain genetic elements can move from one site in a chromosome to another; and when they do, they alter the behaviour of adjacent genes profoundly. Genes previously silent become active, and changes in the pattern of gene expression are generated that produce marked changes in the phenotype – to date, in bacteria, in cultured cells or in the fruit-fly. It would be unwise to regard the problem as solved; it would be equally unwise to regard the lack of a good explanation for the change as a reason why such change could not occur.

Conclusion

We now need to look for an explanation that will correlate

all these facts. My view is that evolution does this well and that the alternative views do not do it well. Special creation does not explain, nor has any need of, biological variation. Why should such variation occur if the world is only 6,000 years old? Indeed, the world appears to be very old, thus explaining also both the variety of geological strata and the wealth of fossil evidence as changing life forms in a changing world. During that long period of time many species have become extinct and the species we now see appear only recently in the fossil record. If species can change (and they can), and the world changes too (and it does – no-one, I think, doubts the changes of the past, from the comparatively recent Ice Ages to the long-term interaction of the tectonic plates and continental drift), then surely the present world and its animal and plant species are different from what existed at the beginning? Different but related, for anatomy, physiology, biochemistry, and now molecular biology, all point to a single origin with subsequent variation. I regard it as most significant that the evolutionary relationships derived from computer-drawn relationships between amino acid sequences in proteins should be so similar to those derived by more conventional methods. If these different criteria had demanded different ancestral trees, then evolution would have been cast in serious doubt; but for a science of the past, such congruence is the strongest kind of evidence we can obtain.

I conclude that, as a scientific theory, evolution is the best so far. It may yet be superseded, but special creation does not seem to be a valid scientific alternative. Special creation derives from one particular understanding of a difficult chapter – Genesis 1 – difficult not with regard to its theological teaching, which is plain, but as to its degree of literalness. With all respect to those who take Genesis 1 literally, I submit that although the theory of evolution has problems of detail, special creation has huge problems, in that it fails to come to terms not merely with the detail but the whole content of several areas of knowledge that are now well-established.

Response to D.C. Burke

D. T. Gish

Professor Burke offers several major postulates in his paper. I submit the following critique of each of these postulates.

1. *The nature of science.* Professor Burke is correct in saying that science treats the world as a vast machine and attempts to find out how it works. Strictly speaking, science can deal only with the here-and-now. Scientists make observations in the real world, and then try to explain what they see. According to this view, all theories of origins are outside of empirical science. Such theories rest on inferences based on circumstantial evidence. There were obviously no witnesses to the origin of the universe or to that of a single living thing.

Neither creation nor evolution is a scientific theory, although each has scientific character, since each process would have had consequences which would be observable today (for example, the fossil record). Inferences based upon such information as that derivable from the fossil record are inherently limited, however, since the process which gave rise to the fossils is not directly observable.

Professor Burke states that scientists distrust dogmatic statements about the world. Perhaps, but not about the *origin* of the world. Evolution is dogmatically stated to be a fact by most evolutionists, and any scientific paper offered for publication in current science journals which even hints at the possibility of creation is almost certain to be rejected. Since increasing numbers of scientists are beginning to recognize the poverty of Darwinism and of its successor, neo-Darwinism, as an explanation for origins, it is true that a scientist who could suggest a plausible naturalistic alternative would be rewarded by his fellow-evolutionists. In contrast to what Professor Burke seems to be suggesting, however, no scientist would ever be rewarded with a Nobel Prize for replacing Darwinian evolution with creation. In the first place, his publications would most likely never see the light of day, certainly not in standard science journals, and secondly he would be ostracized by the so-called scientific community for suggesting creation as an alternative to evolution. One may challenge any particular mechanism of evolution and one may challenge any particular phylogeny, but one must *never* suggest an alternative to evolution itself.

2. *The theological issues.* Professor Burke states that in his view the Christian has no particular stake in whether evolution is true or not. Later on he states that many theistic evolutionists would accept the fact that Genesis 1 teaches a historical Adam and Eve. If Genesis 1 teaches a historical Adam and Eve, there is no doubt that the Christian has a vital stake in whether evolution is true or not. No consistent evolutionist can believe in a literal Adam and Eve, however. Evolutionists believe that mankind gradually evolved from a population of ape-like creatures, resulting in a population of human creatures from which all present-day humans are derived. There is no place in such a system for a literal Adam and Eve. Adam and Eve are merely figurative archetypes in any evolutionary scheme.

Furthermore, the Bible does have much to say about creation. Genesis 1:1 – 2:22 is devoted to the subject of creation, as are numerous other passages of Scripture. Finally, the scientific evidences for the fact of creation comprise a powerful apologetic tool. On the other hand, if we are the product of the chance processes of evolution and properties inherent in matter, who needs God?

In fact, later on in his paper, Professor Burke states that Darwin proposed that all evolutionary changes were slow and gradual for two reasons. First, he could not think of a mechanism to bring about large-scale changes, and secondly, *he did not want to involve divine intervention.* How can one say he believes in 'creation' via evolution, a process devised to be rid of divine intervention?

3. *The evidences for evolution.*

a. Professor Burke mentions variation as an evidence for evolution; later on in his paper he states that creation does not explain, nor has any need of, biological variation. In the first place it is difficult to understand how variation, *per se*, is evidence for evolution; secondly, creation both explains *and* has need of variation. When God created each of the kinds mentioned in Genesis he planned that each kind would spread upon the earth by adapting to various conditions. In order to spread and to adapt to each local environment, as well as to adapt and survive under any future conditions, each created kind would have required considerable variability. This would have involved an initial created genetic variability, or extensive gene pool. Variability would always be limited within the circumscribed boundaries of each kind, however.

I am surprised at Professor Burke's suggestion that the environment of the earth, in the creationist view, has been the same for the past 6,000 years. It has varied greatly during that time, and in fact, varies tremendously from place to place on the earth today. I am also surprised that Professor Burke suggests that new species of dog can arise which cannot interbreed. All varieties of the dog, *Canis familiaris*, are inter-fertile and classified in a single species. In fact, the dog can and does, on occasion, interbreed with coyotes (genus *Canis*), wolves (*Canis lupus*), and jackals (genus *Canis*). All of these creatures apparently are derived from a single created kind, although man has arbitrarily classified them into separate species.

b. Professor Burke mentions that natural selection, acting on hereditary characteristics, is capable of bringing about small-scale variations. No creationist or evolutionist denies that possibility and, in fact, we have just discussed this in the passage above. It is the enormous extrapolation that evolutionists make in suggesting that such a mechanism could derive a man from an amoeba or a duckweed, a palm and an orchid from the same ancestry that creation scientists reject as totally unwarranted, either on the basis of evidence from the living world or evidence from the fossil record.

In fact, late in his paper Professor Burke admits that evolutionists do not know what the mechanisms are that could have resulted in the emergence of new functions, such as the eye, or which could have brought about the supposed transitions that resulted in the different types recorded in the fossil record. Later he states that mutations and gene recombinations may explain minor changes, but are inadequate for the central problem. With this he is turning against neo-Darwinism, the current (although somewhat shaky) dogma, for according to present orthodoxy, mutations and gene recombination along with natural selection are supposed to have been sufficient to convert an amoeba into everything living today, including man.

It is an amazing thing to me that the large majority of scientists are slavishly devoted to a supposed process that they have studied intensely for 120 years; and yet they have failed miserably to establish a mechanism adequate to bring about the process, and their search for historical evidence in the fossil record to document the process has failed even more miserably.

c. Professor Burke mentions geographical distribution as evidence for evolution. It need only be pointed out that evolutionists have no better idea why certain peculiar distributions exist, such as the marsupials in Australia, than do creationists. Both creationists and evolutionists agree that they are there because they migrated there. There is certainly no evidence whatever in the fossil record of Australia to support the idea that marsupials evolved in Australia after their forebears reached there. And why is it that the only other place in the world that the Florida alligator is found is in China?

d. Professor Burke mentions the age of the earth as evidence for evolution. While it is true that evolution demands an immensity of time, and thus any evidence for a young age for the earth or the cosmos would be fatal to evolution theory, evidence that the earth is old would neither prove evolution nor threaten creation. A vast age of the earth is a necessary – but not sufficient – evidence for evolution; and the fact that such a supposition is no threat to creation is self-evident from the fact that many special creationists do believe that the earth is old. There are many good physical chronometers that do seem to establish an upper limit on the age of the earth many orders of magnitude shorter than 5,000 million years, however, and there are many good reasons to question both the methodology and the picking and choosing employed in radiometric dating.

e. I am surprised that Professor Burke cites the fossil record as evidence to support evolution since it is even a greater embarrassment to evolutionists today than it was to Darwin in his day. In fact, Mark Ridley[1] proclaims that no real evolutionist uses the fossil record as evidence in favour of the theory of evolution as opposed to special creation. Since I have dealt with the fossil record in some detail in my own contribution to this book, I will say no more about it here except to note that Professor Burke early in his contribution calls the attention of the reader to the immense wealth of the fossil record, and then late in his paper seeks to explain away the paucity of the transitional forms demanded by evolution, by pleading that we would expect transitional forms to be rare. Actually, in view of the fact that the fossil record has become almost unmanageably rich and evolution is supposedly a continuous process that has produced millions of species by gradual change during the past 3,000 million years, our museums should be overflowing with undoubted transitional forms if evolution is true.

f. Professor Burke cites the evidence for unity of cellular processes and points out that this would be expected by both creationists and evolutionists. In fact, this unity is demanded by creation. If God had created plants with a particular type of amino acids, sugars and nucleotides, animals with other types of these substances, and man with yet other types, what could we eat? We couldn't eat plants. We couldn't eat animals. The only thing humans

[1] Mark Ridley (1981) *New Scientist* 90, 832.

could eat would be each other, and that would not be an acceptable proposition. Thus, plants, animals and man had to be created with the same type of amino acids, sugars and nucleotides, and that would, of course, require similar metabolic processes, including similar enzymes.

To get the phylogenetic trees described by Professor Burke using biochemical data requires, however, as Hoyle and Wickramasinghe have pointed out,[2] a considerable 'massaging of the data'.[3] Furthermore, the phylogenetic tree that one gets is dependent on the particular protein chosen. For example, one would get a phylogenetic tree of vertebrates based on myoglobin that would vary considerably from one based on haemoglobin. In fact, the phylogenetic tree based on cytochrome C shows, as expected, that mammals are closer to reptiles than to amphibians (although there are several serious discrepancies when all the data are compared). It turns out, however, that when the structures of luteinizing hormone releasing hormone from these creatures are compared, mammalian LHRH is identical to that of amphibians but different from that of reptiles, indicating that mammals are more closely related to amphibians than to reptiles. Many similar contradictions to predictions based on evolution theory derivable from such data could be cited.

Evolutionists have always maintained that eukaryotes (animals and plants whose cells contain organized nuclei with membranes, as well as certain organelles such as Golgi bodies, mitochondria and others) had evolved from prokaryotes (single-celled organisms with no organized nucleus or organelles), which include bacteria and blue-green algae. Evolutionists therefore expected to find evidence linking these two types of organisms. Creationists maintained that this was not so, but that there is a large discontinuity between prokaryotes and eukaryotes.

As Professor Burke points out, and as precisely predicted on the basis of the creation model, there is a vast gulf between prokaryotes and eukaryotes. Rather than

[2] F. Hoyle and N. C. Wickramasinghe (1981) *Evolution from Space*.
[3] See for example the paper by Russell F. Doolittle (1981) *Science* **214**, 149–159, to note all the finagling that is required in attempts to make the data fit some preconceived notion of homology.

accepting this as an abject failure of the evolution model, however, Professor Burke proclaims that this development is actually a plus for evolution theory, being more readily explainable by an evolutionary hypothesis! In fact, the evidence so strongly contradicts Professor Burke's suggestion that some evolutionists are frankly stating that the idea that eukaryotes evolved from prokaryotes must be abandoned as untenable.[4] And if eukaryotes did not evolve from prokaryotes, then just where did they come from? As more and more knowledge about molecular biology accumulates, theories on the origin of life as well as Darwinian evolution become more and more untenable.

g. I would like to close this critique with a brief discussion of Professor Burke's comments on flood geology. The Lord devoted three chapters of the book of Genesis to describing the flood and its consequences, so it can hardly be dismissed as unimportant. Furthermore, we read (Gn. 6:11) that the earth was filled with violence and consequently God decreed a universal judgment upon the earth: 'For behold, I will bring a flood of waters upon the earth, to destroy all flesh in which is the breath of life from under heaven; everything that is on the earth shall die'(Gn. 6:17). Later we read that 'Everything on the dry land in whose nostrils was the breath of life died' (Gn. 7:22). Excepted, of course, were those taken on the ark. As to the geographical extent of the flood, we are told 'And the waters prevailed so mightily upon the earth that all the high mountains under the whole heaven were covered' (Gn. 7:19). Now, whatever difficulty one may imagine, or how much or how little of this Scripture one chooses to believe, there seems to be no doubt what the passage is saying. Scripture certainly seems to be describing a universal flood, since a local year-long flood which covered all the mountains and destroyed all land-dwelling, air-breathing creatures is difficult to imagine, and the use of an ark to escape a local flood seems to be absurd when migration would have sufficed just as well.

Professor Burke mentions the difficulty of getting all the animals on the ark, and mentions, among others, whales

[4] James E. Darnell Jr. (1978) *Science* 202, 1257.

and dolphins. As mentioned above, no marine organisms, such as whales, dolphins, marine vertebrates, or fishes, had to go on the ark. Even taking into account all possible extinct and living land-dwelling, air-breathing creatures, the space on the ark would have been adequate.[5] Professor Burke contends that a miraculous migration would be required to get all unique creatures from every island to the ark. First of all, the migration certainly was miraculous, for Noah did not go all around the world gathering two of each kind. In Genesis 6:20 we read that '. . . two of every sort shall come in to you. . .'. Secondly, undoubtedly the geography, geology and the geographical distribution of plants and animals were drastically different before the flood than in post-flood times.

Interpreting earth history presents enormous problems, of course, no matter what model one adopts, the evolutionary uniformitarian model or the catastrophism model. There is much to support the world-wide flood described in the Bible, however. Enormous fossil graveyards, vast sedimentary deposits, volcanic activity on an unimaginable scale, tremendous tectonic movements, the subsidence of the sea-floors and a world-wide mild climate in times past are a few of these evidences. Finally, it can be said that the matter of the flood is not central to the creation/evolution question, since it was an event which occurred subsequent to the origin of the earth and of living things.

To say that there is no evidence to support evolution would be foolish indeed. The overwhelming weight of the scientific evidence is, however, solidly in support of special creation. In view of the evidence that has accumulated and is continuing to accumulate in support of creation, the position of theistic evolution, I predict, will rapidly become anachronistic.

---

[5] See J. C. Whitcomb and H. M. Morris (1961) *The Genesis Flood* (Nutley, N. J.: Presbyterian and Reformed Pub. Co.), pp. 65–69.

7

Issues and dilemmas in the creation - evolution debate

D. G. Jones

A biblical approach to man · Man as an object of naturalistic speculation · Coping with conflict · The attraction of creationism · The interface between creation and science · The question of origins

A biblical approach to man

A central issue in the creation-evolution debate over the last 150 years has been the nature of man. The question can be put as follows: Is man just a product of an evolutionary process, or is he something more?

For Christians, the starting-point is the Bible, which simply asserts that man was created in the image and likeness of God. It then follows that man is not only dependent upon God for all that he is, but that those qualities which are peculiarly human, and which mark us out as persons, reflect characteristics of God himself. Such qualities as man's creativity, rationality, value-systems and self-awareness all signal the special nature of human beings.

But the Bible tells us more; it asserts something which is not obvious, that man is a creature with whom God can enjoy a personal relationship, and that it is man's rejection of this relationship that lies behind the failure of human relationships. Instead of harmony, we see defiance, rebellion, anguish and strife – man is not the creature he should be but is at odds with his Creator, his neighbours and himself.

The Bible also makes clear the relationship between man and the rest of creation: man, like the rest of creation,

198

was created by and is totally dependent upon God – and yet he has been given dominion over the rest of creation. This privilege carries responsibilities; man must exercise his power in line with God's moral nature, for he is no passive spectator in an untouchable world. This means that as his understanding of the world grows, he must use this knowledge in a godly way – rejoicing in its unfolding secrets and using the knowledge for the welfare of mankind. Thus, in some regards, man is like the rest of creation, for example in his anatomy, physiology, biochemistry and in certain behavioural ways; but in other respects is like God, for instance in his dominance over, and responsibility for, other creatures.

As Christians, we agree that man 'does not live by bread alone', but he does need bread, and when it is eaten, it is metabolized in exactly the same way as by the higher primates, and the energy it brings comes by mechanisms common to all living creatures. Christians agree that human life needs a living relationship to God and all agree that he also needs a supply of basic nutrients. It is so easy to stress one at the expense of the other – to be pulled in a 'spiritual' direction, seeing man as a spiritual being and little else, or in a 'naturalistic' direction, so that man becomes a product of nature largely devoid of spiritual connections. In this article I shall explain how I believe we need both these emphases to retain a balanced view.

Man as an object of naturalistic speculation

Once we agree that man is a proper subject for scientific enquiry, then the nature of man immediately becomes the object of naturalistic speculation – by which I mean philosophical speculation bound only by what is discoverable by science. Two major areas have attracted attention – the origin of man and human behaviour.

The study of man's origins has been much influenced by ideas imported from elsewhere in science – and which are therefore, by definition, non-religious in nature. A concept such as chance, which has a limited and defined meaning in genetics and evolution, has been seen not only as the guiding mechanism behind evolutionary mechanisms, but has also been interpreted as a pointer to the meaninglessness of human existence. As a result, what began as a search for the mechanism behind man's physical origin has spilt over into other areas, causing intense unease about the purpose and role of man himself. This transformation of a scientific enquiry into a philosophical statement has properly alarmed Christians and brings the scientific enterprise into disrepute.

When we leave out God and see man purely as a product of nature, he no longer possesses any unique status, and is entirely explicable as a product of evolutionary change. This is because science has become the only source of knowledge. It has therefore lost its neutrality, for science, by definition, cannot take sides as to whether God exists or as to whether God was or was not involved in evolution. Consequently, whenever science is seen as the sole source of knowledge, it inevitably spreads outside the bounds of scientific enquiry, leading to a world-view with no room for faith. But since God was left out at the beginning, it is not surprising that he is not there at the end!

Sir Julian Huxley, writing when scientific humanism was at its height in the 1940s and 1950s, illustrated the tendency very clearly. For him, and for many others, the advance of knowledge made supernaturalism and the idea of God untenable. Quite simply he believed that explanations about the origin and nature of man based on natural processes invalidated explanations involving the supernatural. Huxley regarded evolution as a comprehensively natural, all-embracing process, so that nothing whatever in the universe could exist specifically for man's benefit. Man is alone in the universe, completely natural, utterly autonomous, with no God to worship: he is in the forefront of the procession of earthly living things, working out the rudimentary principles of evolutionary advance.

Huxley, like many others, found it easy to support his philosophical and anti-religious bias by tentative scientific findings. In this way, scientific facts – and especially the hypotheses advanced to explain them – have been readily converted into an evolutionist philosophy, which is almost invariably anti-Christian. This is an illustration of *evolutionary humanism*, which is widespread and is often uncritically accepted, and which moreover constantly intrudes into the creation-evolution debate.

Evolutionary humanism has religious overtones, because it tries to understand what makes man the being he is. In tackling this, the profoundest of all religious issues, it leaves God out of account and aims to answer every question about man and his goals by looking only at man's place in the evolutionary process. Evolution is taken, by definition, as the only yardstick against which man's meaning and worth can be measured. It is not surprising, therefore, that evolutionary humanism's conclusions are very different from the Christian view of man; thinking now starts, not with God, but with a process independent of, and indeed opposed to, God. In this guise evolution becomes a religion of its own which, for many people, serves as a god-substitute.

Coping with conflict

It is hardly surprising that evangelical Christians with a high view of Scripture vehemently oppose evolutionary humanism. Such opposition is relatively easy; what is far more difficult is to know how to put together the two sides of man's nature. While Christians are agreed that man is God's creation, they are not agreed on how to assess the biological aspects of his nature.

Faced with this dilemma, Christians part company. The most obvious solution is to see the problem as yet another manifestation of the old 'Bible versus science' controversy. According to this, the Bible provides infallible data on man, his origin and nature. Science, by contrast, is simply man's own attempts at understanding the perplexities of his existence; man's fallibility is matched only by his arrogance at presuming to undertake such a profound venture. When the question is man's origin, creation is seen as the biblical mechanism and evolution as the scientific one.

Appealing as this scenario may be to some, it fails to come to grips with the real problem. Man is an integral part of nature – this is what creation is all about – and God has given him responsibility for the natural world of which he is a part. And so, a scientific analysis of man, and even of his origins, is a legitimate approach to an understanding of at least some facets of man's nature. The Bible in no way rules out such an analysis; it actually encourages us to study man's place in the natural world and to view our results in the context of God's purposes for the world. Of course, the scientific approach is a limited one and its conclusions are restricted by its method and starting-point.

It is important to realize that the scientific approach is a legitimate one. Virtually all Christians accept this in the physical sciences and in most of the biomedical sciences. Difficulties arise in areas where evolutionary ideas intrude. I am suggesting that evolutionary biology is just as legitimate a form of science as is nuclear physics or ophthalmology. The misuse by some biologists of the data of evolutionary biology – as a support for evolutionary humanism – is not an argument against the legitimacy of those data. The misuse of science warns us against its misuse, not against the scientific endeavour as such. In much the same way the misuse of the Bible by the cults in no way demonstrates that the Bible is worthless; it simply instils into us the importance of a correct interpretation of the Bible.

If science is to be taken seriously, what happens when there is apparent conflict between science and the Bible? What happens in the evolution and creation areas? One thing is certain; conflict cannot be overcome by neatly separating the Bible and science, and presenting an 'either-or' option.

Care has to be exercised in deciding how the terms 'creation' and 'evolution' are used. For instance, it is often assumed to be self-evident that 'creation' describes a supernatural, more-or-less instantaneous act and 'evolution' a natural (and frequently anti-supernatural) gradual progression of events. However, it is not self-evident why creation should be instantaneous, nor why God should not work through, and control, a gradual progression of events.

The way in which the Christian view of human nature has been routed by evolutionary humanism, in the name of science, vividly demonstrates what can happen when the limitations of science are ignored. On the other hand, Christians are also adept at ignoring how biblical data are to be employed by insisting on a totally literal interpretation of the chronology and time-scale of the early chapters of Genesis, and also viewing the world as a totally static system. The end result of this approach are ideas that fail to take seriously the scientific method. What predominates in both instances are the beliefs of the protagonists, evolutionism in one case and creationism in the other. By their very nature, neither is testable; the one affirms the autonomy of man, the other the dependence of man upon God. Each is subject to the presuppositions of the respective belief; neither is trying only to look clearly at the world God has made.

If this is the case, we need to be asking whether there is any way out of this impasse. Is there any way in which Christians can take due account of the contributions of *both* the Bible *and* science, without compromising their faith? More specifically, we need to be asking whether what science says about man's origins and history provides a *real* picture of a *real* world, that is, information about man's past that we are bound to accept. Does it provide data which we should be incorrect to reject, because they are data which are essential for a holistic view of man as both a material and spiritual being?

To tackle these questions we are driven to definitions. *Evolution* refers to a process of change in a particular direction, the extent of this change being limited to individual differences within a single family (individual variation), among different populations of the same species (microevolution), and at a supra-population level to form new species, genera, families and orders (macroevolution). I shall concentrate on the distinction between micro- and macroevolution, or between the special and general theories of evolution, respectively.

This is a distinction between those changes which can be observed (microevolution or special theory), and those which are extrapolations from observations and are inferred to have occurred at a much more general level (macroevolution or general theory) (Fig. 1). Microevolution refers to the relatively small changes occurring in living animals and plants, with the production of new varieties and occasionally new species. Macroevolution, by contrast, asserts that all the living forms in the world today have arisen from a single source which, in turn, was derived from a non-living form. Microevolution, therefore, is a strictly experimental discipline, limited in scope and making relatively few generalizations. Macroevolution is only partially experimental; it is extensive in scope, makes vast assumptions, and suggests far-reaching hypotheses. The former is science in its narrow, disciplined sense; the latter science in its broad, predictive sense. The one is capable of rigorous scientific testing; the other is not and never will be.

Theology	Science	Mechanism	Philosophy
	Evolutionary theory	Microevolution Macroevolution Uniformitarianism	Evolutionary humanism
Creation	Special creation	Flood geology ?Microevolution Catastrophism	Special creationism

Figure 1. Distinction between major terms in the creation-evolution debate

This major distinction within evolution must not be overlooked. It is all too easy to reject evolution as a whole because of disagreement with macroevolution, or to claim that macroevolution is true using the evidence for micro-evolution. Macroevolution makes certain major assumptions; for example, that science can say something about the step from non-life to life, that viruses, bacteria, plants and animals are all related, and that there is a common ancestral stock for all the vertebrates. These are legitimate assumptions within science, although they are not capable of experimental verification and they may be wrong. The question for Christians is whether they are contrary to biblical teaching, especially that contained in Genesis 1–3. If Christians decide that they are, they must first show this and then put forward alternative assumptions which can be used by scientists as an alternative basis for science. These assumptions put forward by Christians will then be open to revision, and perhaps ultimate rejection, in the light of their usefulness or otherwise to the scientific community.

Some Christians fear this approach because the dividing-line between macroevolution and evolutionary humanism is an all-too-tenuous one. Indeed, it is often blatantly ignored by scientists, especially when discussing the status of man. How then do we distinguish between them? This is best done by examining the reliance which is placed on assumptions and speculations. In science the assumptions behind macroevolution are regarded openly as assumptions, their purpose being to hold together a scientific idea long enough for it to be tested, and to provide useful tools. In philosophy, however, the assumptions of evolutionary humanism become indispensable principles and indisputable basic ideas.

How much reliance is placed upon the assumptions and speculations depends upon the religious presuppositions of those involved. For evolutionary humanists they are essential for a unified world-view. For Christians they are useful tools, but tools they are free to accept or reject as the scientific evidence requires. Christians, therefore, should be able to take a more objective view of the scientific evidence than the evolutionary humanist, who depends on the theory of macroevolution as the basis for his philosophy. This means that, in practice, Christians may be freer to analyse micro- and macroevolution objectively, and to draw conclusions about their merits on strictly scientific grounds.

Two provisos must be made. If Christians are to exercise this freedom, they must be experts in the areas under investigation. Armchair theologians have not earned the right to make sweeping pronouncements in geology or anthropology, while simplistic assertions are no substitute for an intimate understanding of what are usually highly complex problems. Christians also have their assumptions, and these may not always be as biblically based as imagined. Christians are not immune to bias, inaccurate information, dubious ways of arguing, and succumbing to group pressure. Such failures are not confined to evolutionists, and Christians need to recognize that they, too, may sometimes be in error.

The attraction of creationism

Just as evolution needs to be viewed from a variety of angles, so does creation. Specifically, the theological doctrine of creation needs to be distinguished from what is sometimes referred to as 'special creationism' (Fig. 1). Put another way, this entails distinguishing between the biblical doctrine of creation, and special creation; the former providing the *theological* basis for a Judaeo-Christian view of the universe and the latter a suggested *mechanism* for the way the world came into existence. Although the two are sometimes regarded as different aspects of the one truth, this is far from assured. All Christians believe in God as Creator, but are they *obliged* to believe that the creation was effected by a series of instantaneous acts? The latter does not follow inevitably from the former, unless it is assumed that the Bible provides all we can know about the theological and scientific aspects of the history of man and his world. If this is not the case, special creation stands or falls on its merits as a scientific explanation of origins, since it proposes a specific mechanism for how man came to be as we know him – an alternative to the evolutionary mechanism. Consequently, it must be judged by the same standards of criticism as evolutionary ideas; it must be supported by experimental data, and it is as liable to modification, transformation and refutation as any legitimate scientific hypothesis. Furthermore, as a healthy scientific hypothesis, it should be supported as much by scientists who are not Christians as by those who are.

The biblical doctrine of creation should, therefore, be held separate from special creation, as a postulated scientific mechanism. For many Christians this is difficult, because special creation appears to point towards God as Creator, in contradistinction to evolution which appears to point away from God towards purposelessness. Understandable as this feeling is, it is based on the proposition that views on *how* things have come into existence point to the *meaning* of existence itself. Not only is this a debatable proposition, but it also elevates, to a position of supreme importance, mechanism rather than meaning. The dangers of this arise from our erring grasp of the scientific mechanism of creation (or evolution), and from overlooking what God has to teach us through the magnificent truth of the *fact* of creation.

To illustrate this, we should consider briefly the biblical doctrine of creation. According to the Bible, creation is a sovereign act of God's power, love and wisdom; it is a reflection of his holiness, and is entirely his own work, by which everything that now is was brought forth from nothing. Above all, it draws a sharp distinction between the Creator and the created, between God himself and all else which depends upon him for existence and sustenance. The character of God ensures that nature will be knowable and, usually, predictable. It is controlled by natural law and has meaning that can be discovered by systematic study. Nature is, therefore, an object of study by which God can be worshipped and enjoyed. This, in turn, opens the road to modern science. Nature, as the creation of a wise, just and dependable God, is no longer at the mercy of the vagaries of malevolent and capricious gods. The distinction between the Creator and the creation means that nature, the creation – unlike the Creator – can be known and controlled; it can be treated with respect and seriousness because it is God's handiwork and its study tells us about an essential aspect of reality.

Since God created the world, it must have a history and a goal. God has purposes for the universe at large, just as he has purposes for mankind. Nature is going somewhere; it is changing; perhaps, in some senses, it is progressing. Negatively, it is not a purposeless cycle of events, going round and round, with no end in view. God is in control of the natural world, as he is in control of human history, and he is working out his purposes through it. Christians, therefore, dare not treat lightly the natural world and the scientific study of it. While it is true that God's creation must never be elevated to a status equal to that of God himself, and while it is true that a study of God's creation will not by itself lead to a knowledge of God, neither must the creation be disparaged, because it is nothing less than a reflection of the handiwork of its Creator.

The biblical doctrine of creation takes us to the very heart of theism. It reminds us repeatedly of the omnipotence of God, of his self-existence, of his character and of his purposes. It was a free act of God, displaying his glory, power, wisdom and goodness. Confronted by the creation we are confronted by theological truths of immense grandeur and significance, truths which are basic to our knowledge of God and his purposes. It constitutes the great fundamental truth of all religious thinking, and without it we lose God and all semblance of meaning in the universe.

It is against this background that we should consider ideas on the mechanism of creation which, however else we may wish to view it, is also a theological truth. It is one of the most basic of Christian presuppositions; we know by faith that the universe was formed at God's command, so that what is seen was not made out of what was visible (Heb. 11:3). No scientific investigation, whether of a creationist or evolutionist hue, can prove this, as it lies outside the territories of any form of science.

The biblical account of creation, therefore, stands on its own. It is accepted or rejected on faith, so that belief in creation is fundamental to Christianity. Put in another way, all Christians are creationists; they believe in creation and their thinking stems from it. No world-view can be Christian without a vigorous affirmation of creation.

But *how* did God create? What methods did he employ? I am suggesting that whatever answers we may give to these questions, the questions themselves are of relatively little significance when compared to the momentous fact that it was God who created out of nothing. The contrast between the fact and the mechanism of creation is the contrast between God's purposes and a human appreciation of observable or inferable events. As the burden of the biblical account is the imparting of theological truths, any other truths being taught by Scripture are subsidiary to these, and are merely offshoots of the theological ones.

By definition, the Bible does not contain scientific truths, although it may, by implication, suggest certain limitations to scientific theorizing. For instance, the 'kinds' of Genesis 1 may prompt Christians to consider very seriously whether there are certain boundaries across which change does not occur. The tentativeness with which I put even this forward is deliberate because, before jumping to this conclusion, caution is called for on a number of counts: (a) careful biblical exegesis is essential; (b) the significance of a passage in theological terms should first be ascertained; (c) theological language should not be directly translated into contemporary scientific language, and (d) the manner in which theological truths are to be incorporated into scientific thought-forms (if at all) requires judicious investigation.

With these cautions in mind, the nature of special creation theories becomes more evident. They are hypothetical, in the same way as macroevolutionary theories are hypothetical. Any assessment of them must employ scientific reasoning, both of the narrow observable variety and of the broader more speculative kind. Special creation and evolution are to be judged, therefore, by the same criteria. As far as possible, the belief-systems so often associated with the two are to be ignored; otherwise, creationism and evolutionism are being compared rather than special creation and evolution.

Underlying special creation is belief in fixity, an idea that held enormous attraction for scientists in the eighteenth and early nineteenth centuries. For them, the world had been constructed by God in a rational way, the unity and stability of the creation lying ultimately within the mind of God. The plan of creation had been laid out over time, its object being the introduction of man. Such ideas were derived from Plato, and reflected an idealistic world-view, with animal species representing discrete acts of the divine intellect. Belief in fixity, therefore, rather than being derived from the early chapters of Genesis, was a Platonic idea and was later amalgamated with biblical literalism. Today, we are so used to viewing Genesis 1 and 2 in terms of fixity, that it is difficult to believe that transition may be an even more valid framework for an interpretation of these chapters.

Special creation today generally starts with the proposition of the creation of the world in six 24-hour days a few thousand years ago. This series of recent creative acts produced a world and its array of living things much like those of today. These creative acts are usually defined as instantaneous and involve neither natural processes nor the use of any pre-existing materials. Frequently today, considerable emphasis is placed on a universal cataclysmic flood (Noachian flood) to account for the existence of fossils, and to support the argument in favour of a young earth.

The divergence of this position from an evolutionary one (including in some respects a microevolutionary one) is highlighted by the short history of the earth (and universe), the emphasis upon the instantaneous formation of new groups of plants and animals, and the reliance upon catastrophism. Also running through much special creationism is the design argument and the use of the concept of an ideal type. A critique of each of these views would be a major task, and that is not my purpose here. What we need is a scientific paradigm incorporating these principles. Such a paradigm would have to justify its usefulness by providing an intellectual atmosphere conducive to productive research throughout biology.

The contrast between special creation and evolution, therefore, is the contrast between two quite different ways of looking at the world at the level of scientific investigation. An important test of which is closer to the truth scientifically should be based on scientific usefulness rather than on religious acceptability.

Now I do not believe it is the prime task of Christians to combat evolutionary thinking by erecting creationist systems capable of scientific analysis. However assured we may be of what the Bible reveals about creation, we cannot be equally assured of its stance on the mechanisms of creation. The biblical writers, even if they imply anything at the level of scientific mechanisms, do so in the form of very general principles. And so, even if we today are able to discern the direction in which these principles are pointing, the task of applying them at a detailed level and in terms of current scientific concepts will involve an enormous amount of speculation. This must inevitably mean that creationist schemes built upon this basis will incorporate a whole host of extra-biblical principles, such as the design and ideal-type arguments, and dependence upon fixity and certainty.

If a system based upon general biblical principles were to be constructed, it would have to face the problem that any such system, however valid at a theological level, cannot by its very nature be open to experimental test and hence cannot be truly scientific. This is because the principles, if they are truly biblical ones, are immutable. They are not dependent upon experimental evidence for their validity, and are not subject to the testing-retesting, proof-disproof process of scientific experimentation. A scheme cannot be both thoroughly biblical and rigorously scientific at the same level of analysis. It may be one or the other; it may be one, and at the same time not contravene general principles of the other. It cannot be *both* without sacrificing some essentially biblical or essentially scientific aspects. Biblical knowledge and scientific knowledge represent different levels of appreciating reality. At the best these two levels are complementary; at the worst they may be contradictory. Whichever they are depends on the integrity and skill with which both biblical exegesis and scientific research are carried out.

The interface between creation and science

The Christian looks to the Bible as his source of revelational knowledge about God, his purposes in the world, the relationship of man to God, and of many other features of these fundamental and eternal issues. There is no other avenue to this knowledge, and there can be no adequate substitute. It is within this context that creation must be viewed, the biblical account of creation providing information about God and his relationship to the world of his own creation. This is knowledge which is unchanging, although our appreciation of even this knowledge may alter in the light of new theological, and possibly scientific, insights. Essentially, however, the most that scientific information can do is to supplement the biblical account.

At the same time, Christians live within a particular scientific milieu, as they also live within certain social and political climates. These aspects of our lives influence our attitudes as much as, or more than, we influence them. The scientific milieu of Western societies is unashamedly evolutionary in character, the dominance of evolutionary thinking having had a profound impact on biological thinking. My argument has been that, if this paradigm is inadequate, it must be replaced by a more satisfactory one. This could be by a creationist paradigm, although, before such a revolutionary transformation could come about, the creationist paradigm would have to prove itself better able to account for the vast range of observations and ideas currently accommodated by evolutionary thinking.

There can be no doubt that the present evolutionary paradigm has inadequacies and freely uses untestable assumptions. Nevertheless, this by itself does not justify abandoning it. Another paradigm has to prove itself and there is no such paradigm in sight at present. Whatever may come, any new paradigm will emerge as a result of original thought and repeated experimentation on the part of scientists. It will also be unlike any previous one, although it will take elements of previous systems and build on them.

Here I have reservations over the special creation paradigm. Rather than being an attempt to look in a fresh way at the creation-evolution evidence, it is a reversion to ideas prevalent in the eighteenth and early nineteenth centuries. In order to appreciate the force of those ideas and the reasons why they fell into disrepute, we have to return to the world of the scientific and theological protagonists of the pre-Darwinian era, to people such as William Paley, Georges Buffon, Georges Cuvier, William Buckland, Charles Lyell, Louis Agassiz and Richard Owen. Special creation as envisaged by many Christians today is a product of the scientific and theological climate of the pre-Darwinian era, and however nostalgically some may wish to return to that period, there is no return. We live in a different intellectual climate and Christians have to respond to the particular demands of the contemporary climate.

The special creation paradigm is also being employed by some to bolster belief in God. However, this involves making faith in God dependent upon alleged scientific evidence, a pitfall tragically exemplified by the misuse of natural theology in the eighteenth century. Dependence upon natural theology led to an increasing use of the intellect in approaching God, until this approach became a substitute for revelation. Without revelation, God had to be known by way of natural theology, and so it was that the heavens no longer declared the glory of God to the eyes of faith. Instead, the heavens were used to *argue for* the wisdom of a Creator. Without this natural theology, Christianity would therefore collapse; for a knowledge of God as Creator rested solely on the evidences of the design and harmony recognized in nature. Thus, if ever design and purpose were removed from the universe, God would be removed as Creator and with that the foundation of Christianity would be gone.

In this natural theology, the proof of the existence of God was based on what science had accomplished, and the proof of his continued activity on what it had not. Inevitably, therefore, as the sphere of science expanded, that of theology receded. Up until the time of Paley, empirical evidence from science had always appeared to lead *towards* God, to the advantage of Christianity. This continued as long as design was generally recognized in nature and as long as the underlying science had a static outlook. However, once chance replaced design and change replaced a static conception of nature as the dominant scientific outlook, the precarious superstructure of natural theology toppled, and with it went the faith.

This historical episode should serve as a warning for us, lest we erect an apologetic in which science is used as the bulwark of special creation, which then assumes a critical role in our belief in creation, and even in Christianity. The Christian faith rests on God and his revelation, never on science, either of the evolutionary or special creation variety.

While the desire for harmony between creation and

science is understandable, all detailed hypotheses must be flexible. This is always the case when dealing with complex and tenuous problems. To adopt rigidly-fixed positions, when many details of biblical interpretation and far more scientific details are controversial, is to court disaster. The adoption of somewhat open-ended positions is essential. Note, however, that this open-endedness is essentially on the scientific issues where open-endedness is mandatory, as even very general scientific principles are subject to revision and, occasionally, rejection. The biblical data, by contrast, are not open-ended, although biblical interpretation of Genesis 1–11 has elements of open-endedness and special creation schemes include debatable philosophical components. In particular, biblical interpreters differ on the meaning of the 'days' of Genesis 1 and on the nature of the chronology of that chapter. The fixity and certainty so characteristic of special creation schemes are not Christian in essence. Even on the religious side, therefore, the matter is not as black and white as is often suggested.

Two applications of this open-endedness principle are relevant here. The first is that we should not expect complete harmony between the different levels of explanation of how God brought the world into existence. Harmony is usually interpreted as meaning that the biblical and scientific levels of explanation are providing exactly the same story in different terminology. However, I do not believe that this is what harmony implies in the creation-evolution debate, for there are internal uncertainties within each level of explanation. If, for the sake of argument, we allowed for the possibility of complete harmony, it would be ephemeral. As the scientific explanation underwent modification, which it must do if it is truly scientific, the harmony experienced today would be a historical relic in the inevitable disharmony of a few years hence. The historical example of natural theology and the design argument illustrate this in a poignantly extreme form. It is arguable, therefore, that complete harmony will ever be achieved in a fallen world, because it demands knowledge and understanding of which humans, including Christians, are incapable.

Our expectations of what harmony between the biblical

and scientific accounts might involve require careful analysis. A critical factor may be that the two point towards the *humanness* of human existence. The accounts should enhance our understanding of man as an integrated being in all his wholeness – spiritual, physical, mental, aesthetic and personal. No one account, whether biblical or scientific, can by its very nature provide a complete picture of man. Neither, however, should any account detract from man as a created being having facets of God's image and likeness.

Using this principle each possible explanatory account of man's origins and history should be investigated afresh. The end result of such an investigation would be, I suggest, both a willingness to take the biblical account of creation very seriously and also a respect for scientific investigations, including ones with an evolutionary premise. On the other hand, evolutionary humanism and even perhaps some forms of special creationism may well be found wanting on account of their respective forms of arbitrary dogmatism.

The second application of the open-endedness principle is that scientific data regarded as valid in scientific circles must be given due weight by Christians. This does not mean, of course, that such data are immutable or that all interpretations based on them will turn out to be correct. It does mean that they should not be lightly dismissed because they do not conform with certain Christian presuppositions. This is a necessary principle if we believe that a study of nature reveals legitimate data about nature – a belief enshrined in the Christian view of nature with its dependence upon the sustaining activity of a reliable and faithful God. Science is an activity in its own right, unencumbered as far as possible by the constraints of religious, philosophical, political and social system-building. While it is evident to us now that science is not a neutral activity and is influenced by general philosophical and social paradigms, nevertheless the obligation remains to remove it as far as possible from the direct influence of these spheres. Once this obligation is overlooked, science is reduced to a subjective, mystical system of little or no objective value.

The relevance of this discussion for the creation-evolution debate is that Christians may have to live with apparent conflict between some features of the biblical and scientific realms. A case in point is the age of the world. Scientific evidence gives the world a great age, whereas biblical interpretation based on the universality of the flood and catastrophism renders it young. The reasons for this discrepancy are not my concern at this juncture; what does concern me is the explanation that the great antiquity of the world is only *apparent*; that is, the apparent age does not correspond to the actual age; the former being the scientifically determinable age and the latter the biblically inferred age.

On this assumption a scientist using the techniques and principles of contemporary geology would be forced to a *wrong* conclusion on the age of the earth. There are no means by which he could detect a young earth which appeared old – God would seem to be involved in trickery. He would have to ignore his own scientific findings or else question the theory of a young earth. I advocate the second.

The concept of apparent age is deceptive and perilous for Christian thinking, introducing as it does a deliberate confrontation between scientific and allegedly biblical positions. The tragedy about confrontation of this type is that it stems from a confusion of biblical and scientific categories. If the young earth position is correct, it should be capable of scientific confirmation and should take its place within the domain of scientific investigation. Similarly, sudden creation, catastrophism and the lack of change within biological processes should all be put to the test of normal scientific procedures. Confrontation between different scientific schemes is healthy *in the scientific arena*, but not when non-scientific issues are also at stake.

The question of origins

The creation-evolution debate continues to occupy a prominent position in Christian circles because of the belief that man's origins determine his present significance.

This implies that man's ancestry determines his nature, so that a subhuman past signifies a less-than-fully-human present. It also appears to be widely assumed that man's ancestry as a species will affect what he believes about his destiny as an individual.

This stance is characterized by the surreptitious interplay of scientific and religious data. The origins of any biological or physical system lie in the past, often the remote past, so that they are not subject to conventional scientific investigation. The events constituting the beginnings of such a system are neither observable nor repeatable. In many instances they were unique, with the result that all attempts at reproducing analogous events are tinged with a profound element of uncertainty. Consequently, the further an event lies in the past, the greater the uncertainty attached to it and the greater the part played by presuppositions.

It is essential to take account of the respective roles of data and presupposition in questions of origins. It is vitally important to determine whether God or some other agency lies behind this world, and whether man is the epitome of God's creation or simply a chance product of an impersonal cosmic force. This the religious issue. Alongside this, however, must be placed the scientific questions of mechanism. Even for the remote past there are data to be observed and interpretations to be made; this remains the realm of scientific analysis, albeit a sometimes tenuous one when origins are under investigation. The *mechanism* of man's own past is a legitimate field for scientific enquiry, and does not by itself have consequences for the *nature* of man, as long as the scientific-mechanistic and religious-philosophical domains are recognized as distinct levels of understanding.

Unfortunately, this distinction is frequently overlooked, with claims such as 'man has risen, not fallen'. This is the outcome of converting a scientific hypothesis about origins into a naturalistic statement about man's nature, a common although not inevitable fallacy in this difficult realm. The pitfalls of discussions about origins are many, highlighting the imprecision of the scientific data and the plethora of speculation surrounding the data. There is no way around this dilemma, and I wonder whether we should not be paying more attention to the contemporary world than to the unsatisfactory world of the remote past.

Perhaps I can best illustrate my suggestion by reference to our view of man. An *origins approach* to man is, in the climate of the late twentieth century, an evolution-based approach which in the hands of evolutionary humanists leaves little room for God and minimizes man's distinctive characteristics. Man is seen as part of a naturalistic, closed universe, with no 'way out' to God and no 'way in' from God. Man's relationship is solely with the world of nature, from which he achieves whatever significance he can acquire.

The majority of Christian apologists, faced with this world-view, feel obliged to do battle with biologists over their view of both evolution and man. This has led many Christians into a general hostility towards science and, because of their fear that the Christian view of man is being engulfed by evolutionary humanism, into a concerted attack on the validity of all evolutionary ideas. From this has arisen the equation of anti-evolutionism with orthodox Christian ideas, and the further equation of anti-evolutionism with special creation.

This is a dangerous impasse from which there is no escape, as the status of man and even the existence of God have been made wholly dependent on the question of origins. A Christian apologetic thus revolves around challenging the data of micro- and macroevolution, in an attempt to disprove the validity of evolutionary humanism.

This end result can be avoided only by adopting some of the approaches to this debate suggested in previous sections. I suggest that it would be wiser to devote more attention to what we know about man in his contemporary setting. This is a *contemporary approach*, the baseline for which is provided by God's revelation of man's status, our biological, social and behavioural understanding of man, and our awareness of what it means to be human. It takes contemporary man as the starting-point and recognizes his place in a universe open to God, who is both the creator and upholder of all that man holds dear.

The contemporary approach offers at least some guidelines on man and his relation to evolutionary theory. At a scientific level, we may be able to learn from evolutionary approaches to man, since a biological understanding of man is relevant to a holistic appreciation of the human situation. This level must not be confused, however, with the biblical one, which alone can direct man in his relationship to God and indicate the future directions he should take. The tension between biblical revelation and biological understanding is a real one. Nevertheless, together they provide the means for increasing man's knowledge and supplying him with the tools necessary to come to terms with his environment, himself and God.

Response to D.G. Jones

E. H. Andrews

Since Gareth Jones does not actually advance a case for evolution in his article, nor one against 'creationism', it is difficult to provide a clear-cut criticism of his essay. What he has done, I would suggest, is to propose a new philosophical framework in which he hopes the debate between evolutionists and creationists will assume a more constructive character. Before we look at this proposed framework, however, we need to consider some of the claims made in preparation for it, concentrating of course upon those statements which a creationist would feel obliged to question.

These are as follows:

1. Evolution can be divorced from its philosophical or religious implications. Christians can separate science and its findings from their beliefs.

2. Evolutionary science is just as legitimate a form of science as is nuclear physics (for example). Evolutionary concepts, although not susceptible of proof, constitute 'legitimate assumptions' within science.

3. A distinction can be drawn between the doctrine of creation and that of 'special creation', the former relating to the fact and the latter to the mechanism of creation.

Let us consider these points in turn.

Response to D. G. Jones

Can evolution be divorced from its philosophical or religious implications?

Evolution, it is claimed, is a legitimate science which can be employed as a convenient hypothesis for serious biological research without any atheistic overtones. (I fully accept the distinction between macro- and micro-evolution, and in what follows 'evolution' should be taken to refer to the former. Most creationists are happy to allow considerable variation within the created kinds.)

I cannot agree with the idea that evolution can be separated from its theological implications. The essence of evolutionary theory is that origins can be explained by the operation of scientific law without appeal to the miraculous. In biblical terms this means that origins are attributable to the providence of God rather than to the creative acts of God. Indeed, the concept of 'creation' vanishes altogether on this view, apart of course from the *ex nihilo* creation itself. The creationist argues that Scripture clearly distinguishes creation from providence and does not limit the former to the initial creative fiat. The Genesis teaching of a finished creation is, alone, sufficient to establish this point. While the Christian evolutionist replaces creation by providence, his non-Christian counterpart naturally takes advantage of the elimination of the idea of creation to infer the non-existence of God. And who can blame him, since the concept of providence is derived from that of creation, as I have shown elsewhere?[1]

My quarrel with theistic evolution, therefore, is far more fundamental than an argument over the evidence for evolution, or even the methods by which this evidence is interpreted. It is the fundamental idea, that scientific enquiry can provide a complementary and independent world-view to that of Scripture, that I am forced to reject. Yet it is to just such a 'complementarity' that Gareth Jones appeals when he suggests that we can have evolution as a science without any theological implications. It is not sufficient to argue that biblical paradigm and terminology are different from their scientific counterparts. This is true, but it does not follow that revelation and science can be

[1] E. H. Andrews (1980) *God, Science and Evolution* (Welwyn: Evangelical Press), pp. 45–63.

kept in watertight compartments. It is our responsibility, as believers in revelation, to explain how the two relate to each other. In particular, we must point out that the Bible teaches quite specifically that scientific law is the 'word of his power' by which God 'upholds all things' (Heb. 1:3), and that miraculous creation sets a limit to the application of scientific enquiry to the subject of origins (indeed, to the subject of miracles in general).

Gareth Jones criticizes both the philosophical extension of evolution propagated by scientific humanists and the literalism that he thinks typifies the 'special creationist'. 'What predominates', he writes, 'are the beliefs of the protagonists, evolution . . . and creationism . . . neither is trying to look clearly at the world God has made.'

But in the light of Romans 1:20–23 and 1 Corinthians 1:19–21, the Christian must surely declare that no-one can look 'clearly' at the world without the help of God's revelation. It is only as we bring to bear the truths learnt from Scripture that we can ever understand the physical universe in which we live. It is quite wrong to suggest that Christians should suspend their beliefs when they come to consider the realm of science. This is the essence of 'complementarity' and it is totally unbiblical. Of course, the beliefs we bring to bear in our interpretation of the findings of science must be genuinely derived from Scripture. The creationist must indeed demonstrate that what he believes is really what the Bible teaches. If his interpretation of Scripture is at any point doubtful, he must be honest enough to admit this and suspend judgment on the issue. But assured biblical beliefs cannot be set aside just because the question under discussion happens to be 'scientific' rather than, say, historical, social or philosophical.

This essential point is often misunderstood because scientific investigation (just like the study, say, of history) can be conducted without any explicit reference to God or the spiritual realm. In spite of the scriptures cited, unsaved men can arrive at correct conclusions in their scientific work. But this is simply because science is essentially a description of nature, not an explanation. The derivation of scientific laws and theories, as well as their application to human needs in technology, do not require the scientist to ask 'why' but merely 'how' things work the way they do. I can describe a building without any knowledge of, or reference to, the architect or even the purpose for which he designed the edifice in question. Similarly, science does not ask the questions: 'Why are the laws of science so? What are their purpose?' And as long as science limits itself to a purely descriptive role it requires no faculties other than natural ones. Most science is of this character; the mould is broken only when science seeks to 'explain' origins, that is, to pass comment on events that are not experimentally observable. (I am not, of course, referring to comment on observable past events such as the fossil record, but to such interpretations of that record as attribute it to evolutionary processes that cannot be observed.)

This leads us to our second question.

Is evolutionary science as legitimate a form of science as, say, nuclear physics?
We must first understand what is meant by 'evolutionary science'. If this expression refers to such things as the study of fossils, the field study of natural selection or the laboratory investigation of mutations, there is no disagreement. Such activities are totally valid as experimental science. If, on the other hand, the phrase means the interpretation of observed phenomena in terms of an evolutionary model which contradicts revelation, then the Christian must reject it. The non-Christian is under no such constraint, of course, and one may ask how religious belief has managed to intrude into science in this manner. The answer is that the evolutionary model, although appearing to be just another scientific hypothesis, is really nothing of the kind. A genuine hypothesis is a provisional framework of ideas which permits the further development of experimentally verified conclusions. By Gareth Jones's own admission, evolutionary concepts are 'not capable of experimental verification' and therefore fail the basic test of a scientific hypothesis. Evolution is thus a philosophical theory, and is thus capable in principle of clashing with religious belief.

E. H. Andrews

*Can a distinction be drawn between 'creation' and
'special creation'?*
This distinction is clearly central to the theistic evolution
position. But is it valid for the Bible-believing Christian?
To answer this question let us first ask why we believe in
creation at all. The answer must be that the Bible states
that 'in the beginning God created the heavens and the
earth'. We believe in creation because it is plainly taught
by Scripture and for no other reason. But it is for precisely
this same reason that creationists believe in special
creation! To take one incontrovertible point, the Bible
states that the creative process is complete, not ongoing
as evolution requires (Gn. 2:1–3). Are we to believe
Genesis 1:1 but not Genesis 2:1?

Of course, some details of the creationist view are open
to debate, such as the length of the seven days of creation.
Such issues may be matters of interpretation and opposing
views may legitimately be held. But there is enough that
is beyond question in Scripture, to eliminate evolution as
the mechanism of creation, and I have elaborated this
argument elsewhere in this volume. I conclude, therefore,
that the distinction between creation and special creation
is, for the Bible-believing Christian, a false one.

A new philosophical framework?
We come finally to the hope expressed by Gareth Jones
that a new framework of ideas can be established to reconcile the viewpoints of evolutionary science and creationism. This framework would depend upon our taking
an 'open-ended' view, in which both evolution and special
creation are seen as hypotheses to be questioned and
subjected to experimental verification. A new approach
may thus be found which 'takes contemporary man as the
starting-point and recognizes his place in a universe open
to God'. I must leave it to the reader to judge whether
such an approach can be considered in any way biblical, or
whether it is an example of the extra-scriptural philosophy
which Gareth Jones condemns throughout his article.
Surely the biblical methodology must take God the
Creator as its starting-point, and revelation as its touch-
stone. No discipline of human knowledge, not even

science, must be considered a 'no-go area' for revelation. This is especially important when we remember the fallen nature of man and his impaired natural understanding. Gareth Jones is really offering us only a disguised version of complementarity, a theory which fails lamentably to solve the problems and which dangerously undermines the historical and factual validity of biblical revelation.

8
The biblical and philosophical case for special creation

E. H. Andrews

*Introduction · Conflicts between evolution and
the Bible · Creation, miraculous or natural? ·
Creation and science: a synthesis · Conclusion*

Introduction

Although much has been written on the scientific aspects
of the creation versus evolution debate, relatively few
recent authors have considered the matter at the philosophical level. Yet there are two very good reasons for so
doing. Firstly, it is only at this level that common conceptual ground exists for the scientific and biblical viewpoints.
The Bible makes no direct contribution to a discussion,
say, of genetic mutations or electromagnetic theory,
neither has science anything to say about the origin of
matter or the doctrine of the Holy Spirit. There is no self-
evident meeting-point between the two at the basic levels
of pragmatic science and spiritual truth. Indeed this realiz-
ation has led to the idea that there exists a 'complementarity' between the scientific and religious world-views in
which both represent more or less complete and self-
contained descriptions of reality. There is, however, a
deeper level at which common conceptual ground does
exist, and it is the weakness of 'complementarity' that it
fails adequately to explore this ground. This is the level at
which we ask, 'What is the nature of science and scientific
theory? Whence are the laws of science? Why are they as
they are, and not otherwise? How far does scientific theory
describe reality? What are the ultimate limitations of
science?' It is also the level at which we discuss the theo-

logical concepts of creation *ex nihilo*, miracles and providence, as well as the extent of the authority and inspiration of Scripture. These are philosophical questions and *only on this plane* is it ultimately relevant to compare and contrast the testimonies of science and the Bible.

Secondly, as I hope to demonstrate, the conflict between the concepts of creation and evolution is, in the final analysis, not a case of science versus religion but of one philosophy against another. It is a self-evident fact, which is none the less frequently ignored, that no scientific theory or experiment can prove that chemical evolution or neo-Darwinian transformation have actually occurred historically. They can at best provide a rational basis for the *belief* that these processes occurred. I submit therefore that the creationist and evolutionist are alike in exercising faith in (different) interpretations of nature which are not susceptible of scientific proof.

In order to address ourselves to these matters at the biblical and philosophical levels we need to consider a number of related matters. These will by no means exhaust the subject and in some areas may not lead us to clear-cut answers. They will, however, serve to introduce us to a level of debate which may clarify many of the issues and demonstrate the creationist position on origins to be both rational and scientific in the deepest sense of that word.

In what follows, we are going to look first at the conflicts which exist, to the writer's mind, between the biblical and evolutionary accounts of origins, both biological and abiogenic. These conflicts do not, as some imagine, reside exclusively in an unduly literal interpretation of Genesis 1 and 2, but involve the total world-view of Scripture in both Old and New Testaments. It is for this reason that I use the word 'philosophical' to describe the level of debate involved in this conflict.

The reader is referred elsewhere for a fuller treatment.[1,2,3]

[1] E. H. Andrews, in *The Bible under attack* (Welwyn: Evangelical Press, 1978), p. 52.

[2] E. H. Andrews, *Is evolution scientific?* (Welwyn: Evangelical Press, 1977).

[3] E. H. Andrews, *From nothing to nature* (Welwyn: Evangelical Press, 1978).

E. H. Andrews

Conflicts between evolution and the Bible

There are both Christian creationists and evolutionists who, equally, accept that the Bible as originally written is a unique, inspired revelation from God to man, mediated through human authors who were not only guided positively in their writing, but also protected from error. We reject the compromise view of inspiration which has recently gained some currency, that the Scriptures are infallible as regards spiritual truth but contain errors of fact and history arising from the scientific and historical ignorance of the writers.[4,5] We also reject the view that much of the Old Testament is mythological, both in the normal sense of that word and in the theological sense of myth as a non-historical vehicle for spiritual truth. It is a unique feature of the Christian religion that its spiritual teaching is inextricably bound up with human history and stands or falls by the accuracy of its historical record. The most obvious example is the death and resurrection of Jesus Christ, the historicity of which events form the basis of the Christian gospel. But the historical reality of creation is equally basic to the character of God as revealed in Scripture (see for example, Pss. 33:6; 90:2; 104:24; 148:2–5; Is. 40:25–29; Am. 4:13; Rom. 1:25). If creation is, historically speaking, a myth, then the credentials of the God of the Bible are irretrievably destroyed.

The questions that remain, therefore, are:

a. Whether the accounts of and references to creation recorded in Genesis and other parts ·of Scripture are *intended* to be read as sober history; or whether, instead, they are allegorical and poetical without claiming to give factual details;

b. Whether the biblical teaching on creation, providence, the fall and the flood can be reconciled with evolutionary concepts. The answer to this may, of course, depend greatly on our answer to *a.*

Let us examine these questions.

[4] H. R. Jones, in *The Bible under attack* (Welwyn: Evangelical Press, 1978), pp. 9–26.

[5] D. A. Young, *Creation and the flood* (Grand Rapids: Baker Book House, 1977), pp. 17–22.

The biblical and philosophical case for special creation

The historicity of Genesis

It is a basic principle of biblical interpretation that the nature of any piece of writing it contains can be ascertained. Thus poetry, allegory, parable and history must each be recognizable as such either by virtue of its internal structure, its context or on the evidence of other portions of Scripture. On each of these tests, the early chapters of Genesis emerge as unmistakably historical in intent.

The major passages involved are, of course, Genesis chapters 1–3, which contain the accounts of creation and the fall, and chapters 6–9 covering the story of Noah and the flood. The internal structure of these passages is that of a straightforward narrative, with no evidence of typical Hebrew poetical forms[6] and no 'commentary' to suggest that the events described should not be taken factually (as, for example, in Nu. 23:7f. and Jb. 27:1). It has been suggested that the thematic repetition in Genesis 1 ('and the evening and the morning . . .') is indicative of poetical content. But repetition of a theme is common in Hebrew narrative, other examples being: 'These are the generations . . .' (Gn. 2:4; 5:1; 6:9; 11:10; 11:27, etc.); 'All the people shall . . . say, Amen' (Dt. 27:15–26); 'Blessed (cursed) shalt thou be' (Dt. 28:3, 4, 5, 6, 16, 17, 18, 19). Thematic repetition is therefore a device of Hebrew literature indeed, but carries no implications of an allegorical treatment of the subject-matter.

Another proposal[7] developed by Noordtzij[8], Ridderbos[9] and Kline[10], and known as the 'framework hypothesis', suggests that Genesis 1 is not chronological but parallel. Thus Days 1 and 4 deal with 'the realm of light', Days 2 and 5 with the realm of 'water' and Days 3 and 6 with the realm of 'land'. Thus, it is proposed, Genesis 1 is a topical rather than chronological account of creation, with

[6] J. O. Buswell, *A systematic theology of the Christian religion* (Grand Rapids: Zondervan, 1962), p. 140.

[7] J. D. Davies, *Dictionary of the Bible* (Philadelphia, 1898), p. 147.

[8] A. Noordtzij, *Gods Woord en der Eeuwen Getuigenis* (Kampen: J. H. Kok, 1924).

[9] N. H. Ridderbos, *Beschouwingen over Genesis 1* (Kampen: J. H. Kok, 1963).

[10] M. G. Kline, 'Because it had not rained', *Westminster Theological Journal* 20, 1958, 146–157.

the further implication of a 'less historical' and more allegorical character. But such a parallelism surely exists more in the minds of the interpreters than in the text. For one thing, any symmetry which might exist in the passage is broken by the seventh day, while the deliberate numbering of the days is surely intended to convey *sequence* if nothing else! A full refutation of the framework hypothesis has been offered by E. J. Young.[11]

A further argument against a poetical or allegorical reading of Genesis 1 lies in the fact that the Scriptures contain *elsewhere* such poetical descriptions of creation. Psalm 104: 1–23 is clearly based on the Genesis account of creation. It is not only cast in a poetical form, but employs the universal devices of poetic writing such as metaphor (verses 1–5), simile (verse 6), anthropomorphism (verses 13, 19) and so on. We do not really suppose the psalmist to think that God uses clouds as literal chariots or occupies some stratospherical chamber from which he decants water upon the earth. This is evidently poetry. Another such passage is Job 38, where creation is described by such metaphors as a builder laying the foundations of a house, a stellar oratorio, and birth from the womb. All this is obvious and very beautiful poetry, wholly distinct from the unembroidered 'action' language of Genesis 1. Quite apart from the self-evident literary contrast is the consideration that poets frequently celebrate historical events in their verse, but seldom write poems about other poems! The Psalms in particular dwell upon the historical records of Israel or the historical (that is, real life) experience of the writers. By analogy one would expect the creation poems of Psalms and Job to be based upon factual recorded history rather than pre-existent allegory.

Let us look, secondly, at the context of the passages in question. We have already argued that the internal structure of Genesis 1–3 and 6–9 provides no support for a non-historical interpretation, and we now turn to the second criterion of historicity. The accounts of both

---

[11] E. J. Young, *Studies in Genesis One* (Philadelphia: Presbyterian and Reformed Publishing Co., 1964), pp. 43–76.

creation and flood are set in the uncompromisingly historical context of the entire book of Genesis. No-one, I think,
denies the historicity of Abraham and the Patriarchs, nor
is the historical intent of chapters 4–5 in question,
containing as they do the pre-Noachian genealogy. This
genealogy is incorporated into the lineage of Christ in
Luke 3 and is unquestionably regarded as historical by
that careful chronicler. Not only is this historical section,
Genesis 4–5, sandwiched between the creation story and
the flood narrative, but the whole of Genesis is bound
together as a unity by the periodic repetition of the expression: 'These are the generations of . . .' or similar words.
This refrain occurs in 2:4; 5:1; 6:9; 10:1; 11:10; 25:12;
36:1; 37:2 and joins the creation and flood narratives,
indissolubly, to the acknowledged historical sections of
Genesis. Only chapter 1 might (on some view) be held to
lie outside the historical framework established by this
formula, but it would seem quite illogical for the writer
of Genesis to have attached an allegorical preface to what
is otherwise a uniformly historical narrative. We therefore
maintain that the creation and flood epics are, from their
context, wholly historical in intent.

Finally we apply the third criterion of historicity, namely
the testimony of other Scriptures. Firstly, the argument
from silence is not without force. Nowhere in Old or New
Testaments is there the slightest suggestion that Adam,
Noah, the creation or the flood are figurative or mythological. For example, the apostle John provides himself
with an excellent opportunity for reinterpreting the
creation story when, in the prologue to his Gospel, he
identifies Christ as the 'Logos', the agent of God's creative
activity. Yet he not only implies a literal creation but
actually borrows his phraseology from Genesis 1:1. Again,
the apostle Paul employs the physically creative action of
Genesis 1 to illustrate the spiritually creative work of
salvation. 'God, who commanded the light to shine out
of darkness, hath shined in our hearts, to give the light of
the knowledge of the glory of God in the face of Jesus
Christ' (2 Cor. 4:6, AV). The clear implication is that Paul
accepted Genesis 1:3 as a historical event, for otherwise
it loses all force as an illustration of the spiritual fiat of

regeneration.

Peter adds his testimony in 2 Peter 3:3–8. Not only does he refer to the creation story ('by the word of God the heavens were of old, and the earth standing out of the water') but also to the deluge ('the world that then was, being overflowed with water, perished'). Nor is this an isolated statement, for the same writer elsewhere (1 Pet. 3:20) uses Noah and his salvation in the ark to illustrate both God's judgment and deliverance in the spiritual realm.

The historicity of Adam and Eve, and of the fall, is attested by Paul in Romans 5:12–21. It is not sufficient to dismiss this passage by saying, as some do, that Paul was simply using the 'Adamic myth' to bring home a spiritual lesson. The historical reality of the disobedience of one man is essential to the argument being presented here. Indeed it is also essential to insist that the one man in question was the unique ancestor of the human race, for otherwise 'death' could not have 'passed upon all men' and the doctrine of original sin would be negated. If Christ and Moses ('Death reigned from Adam to Moses') are characters of history, the conclusion is inescapable that Adam was also. If Christ's act of atonement is an event embedded in the matrix of human history, so also was Adam's act of rebellion. The apostle, at least, seems under no illusions at this point.

We see, then, that by the tests of internal structure, context and biblical testimony, the Genesis accounts of creation and the flood must be taken as entirely historical in intent. Those theistic evolutionists who teach otherwise do so on criteria that are wholly extra-biblical, as D. A. Young has argued convincingly.[12] The criteria in question are, for example, the presupposition that the Bible is accurate only on matters of spiritual truth and not of science or history. More fundamentally, perhaps, such commentators, though sometimes evangelical in name, implicitly elevate the ultimate authority of human reason above the final authority of Scripture. Thus they feel quite *free* to adopt criteria of biblical interpretation which are

[12] D. A. Young, *op. cit.*, pp. 23–41.

extraneous (and antagonistic) to the rules provided by Scripture itself. A prime example of this kind of treatment is the idea, forcefully expounded by Bernard Ramm,[13] that the Genesis flood was a local phenomenon, in spite of categorical assertions both in Genesis 6–9 and 2 Peter 3 of its universality! The argument adopted is that the geological record (as interpreted by uniformitarian science) contains no evidence of a universal inundation and that the biblical testimony must be reinterpreted accordingly. Such attempts lead to a total contradiction of the actual statements of the Scripture and thus, at the very best, an abandonment of the rule of the perspicuity of Scripture.

In short, any attempt to deny the historicity of the early chapters of Genesis leads to quite insoluble problems of biblical interpretation throughout Old and New Testaments. For the liberal theologian, of course, this does not matter; for he has no time for the doctrine of verbal inspiration. For the theologically conservative, however, the concession (often unconscious) that modern scientific theories must take precedence over the plain meaning of Scripture is the beginning of a slippery slope indeed. It is not sufficient, as some seem to think, to say that the Bible is not a scientific textbook and should not therefore be accorded authority in the interpretation of nature. If Genesis is *history*, then regardless of the particular paradigm employed to record the historical events, the biblical testimony on creation and historical geology *must* be taken into account (and, indeed, conceded the primary place) in the construction of our cosmogenetical world-view.

Can we reconcile the biblical and evolutionary viewpoints?

Having concluded that the creation and flood narratives of Genesis must be read as history, we now address the second question posed earlier. Is it possible to reconcile the biblical accounts with the modern evolutionary world-view? Many Christians who accept that Genesis *is* history

[13] B. Ramm, *The Christian view of science and Scripture* (London: Paternoster Press, 1955), p. 164.

claim that such a reconciliation is possible.

Before we approach the question of reconciliation, we must obviously set out the areas of apparent conflict. These are concisely stated as follows.

a. The age of the earth, and the time-scale of the fossil record, are reckoned in terms of thousands of millions of years by evolution and uniformitarian geology. This is in contrast to the seven-day creation cycle and the genealogical records of Genesis, which seem to place the creation of Adam no more than about 10,000 years ago, even admitting that the genealogies are incomplete.

b. According to conventional thinking, evolution is a continuing process operating now just as it has always operated in the past. In contrast, the creation recorded in Genesis was complete and finished at some past juncture ('on the seventh day God ended his work which he had made', Gn. 2:2).

c. Evolution envisages a continuous improvement of the biosphere, as more complex and adapted forms of life arise with the passage of time. Though temporary setbacks are not ruled out, evolution has a general 'upward' tendency away from imperfections (poor adaptation) towards perfection (total adaptation). In contrast, the creation recorded in Genesis was originally perfect ('God saw every thing that he had made, and, behold, it was very good', Gn. 1:31). However, as a consequence of Adam's fall, the whole of nature has undergone degeneration ('cursed is the ground for thy sake . . . Thorns also and thistles shall it bring forth to thee', Gn. 3:17–18; 'the whole creation groaneth and travaileth in pain together until now', Rom. 8:22, AV), but will one day be restored ('the creation itself also will be set free from its slavery to corruption . . .' Rom. 8:21, NASV). In particular, the fall is an essential ingredient in the Bible's presentation of salvation through Christ.

d. Theistic evolution allows only a single creation miracle, namely the creation *ex nihilo* of matter and energy. The Genesis account appears to involve a succession of miraculous creative acts, each prefaced by the words: 'And God said, Let . . .'.

e. As a corollary of *d.*, evolution appeals only to natural law and process as an explanation of the appearance of life, its diversification and the rise of man, while the Bible suggests that divine fiat was necessary not only for creation *ex nihilo* but also for the creation of life from non-life, the creation of separate life forms and the origin of man.

f. A miraculous creation and fall explain the moral problem of sin and suffering. The theistic evolutionary world-view requires that chance, suffering and cruelty (for example, the survival of the fittest) are intrinsic parts of God's creative activity, thus posing insoluble moral questions.

There may well be points of difference between the creationist and evolutionary world-views which do not appear in the above list, or which could have been made more explicit, but these six issues certainly comprehend the major conflicts which confront us as we approach the problem of reconciling current 'scientific' theories of origins with the testimony of Scripture. Before dealing with these conflicts in greater detail I would like to make a general point, namely, that so much effort has been devoted to the question of the age of the earth, both by creationists and theistic evolutionists, that the other five areas of conflict enumerated above have been largely ignored. Yet, in the writer's view, these more theological and philosophical questions are by far the most important ones. Even if one of the simpler methods of reconciling the time-scales of evolution and Genesis, such as the day-age theory, were universally accepted, the five areas of conflict denoted *b.* to *f.* would remain acute. Until theistic evolution can offer solutions to *these* problems, the evolutionary world-view must remain antagonistic to the general teaching of the Bible.

The age of the earth

In this section we are not concerned to question the conventional geological time-scale, but only to see how far the biblical record can be reconciled with it. We shall look more closely at the scientific validity of 'geological time' in a subsequent discussion. Since whole books have been written on this subject, we can here only outline the attempts that have been made to reconcile a six-day

creation with the thousands of millions of years demanded
by current geological and evolutionary thinking.

Firstly, and most simply, the 'days' of Genesis 1 may
be taken as long periods of time (the 'day-age' theory).
This viewpoint has been set out succinctly by Buswell[14]
and recently reviewed and advocated by D. A. Young[15]
who, as a geologist, is committed equally to the historicity
of Genesis and to the geological time-scale. It has been
reviewed and rejected by Fields.[16] The main argument in
support of the day-age theory is that the seventh day, on
which God rested from his creative work, is still in
progress and thus must represent an epoch rather than a
literal 24-hour day. If this is so, of course, there is no need
to insist that the first six days are literal days either.
Against this interpretation it may be argued that the
expression 'God rested' can be taken to mean 'God
ceased', or 'God began to rest' referring to an instantaneous event which could indeed have occurred on a
literal seventh day. The implied translation of 'God rested'
as 'God rested throughout the seventh day' is required
neither by the text nor by the Jewish sabbath which cele-
brates the completion of creation. Indeed the full statement
is: 'On the seventh day God ended his work which he had
made; and he rested on the seventh day from all his work
. . .' (Gn. 2:2). This seems to imply that both the 'ending'
and the 'resting' were completed, instantaneous actions
without any extension in time. The verb 'to end' *must*
carry this instantaneous significance and 'to rest' *may* also
do so. If this is the case, the seventh day could clearly be
a literal day, and the chief support for the day-age theory
collapses.

Creationists also argue that the Hebrew word *yom*
always signifies a literal day unless the context demands
otherwise[17] and that reference to 'evening and morning'
points clearly to an alternation of day and night such as
normal days would require. The division of light from

[14] J. O. Buswell, *op. cit.*, pp. 133–147.
[15] D. A. Young, *op. cit.*, pp. 81–89.
[16] W. W. Fields, *Unformed and unfilled* (Nutley, N. J. : Presbyterian
and Reformed Publishing Co., 1976).
[17] W. W. Fields, *op. cit.*, pp. 168–179.

darkness (Gn. 1:4) would also be most naturally construed in terms of the earth being illuminated from one direction so that half the globe was in darkness and half in light. This again implies that a day was the period of rotation of earth on its axis. In summary, therefore, the internal evidence for the day-age theory is tenuous in the extreme and the 'normal day' interpretation is most consistent with the usage of *yom* and with the various details of the narrative. Having said this, no-one can claim that the matter is proven either way. The writer *could* have intended a figurative use of *yom*, although there really is no convincing internal evidence in favour of the idea. Furthermore, the day-age theory leads to an unnatural interpretation of the succession of light and darkness and their mutual separation as described in Genesis 1. That is, they too must become figurative, and where does one stop?

The second major attempt to reconcile the biblical and geological time-scales resides in the 'gap theory', which proposes that the geological ages are encompassed between verses 1 and 2 of Genesis 1. Verse 2 is then read to mean: 'And the earth *became* without form and void,' signifying a judgment and destruction of a formerly created and populated earth. The fossil record, it is claimed, dates from this stupendous judgment. The 'creation' described in the remainder of Genesis 1 then becomes a recent recreation in seven literal days. The 'gap theory', popularized by footnotes in the Scofield Bible, has been reviewed and refuted at length in a recent book by W. W. Fields[18], and the reader is referred to that work for further detail. In brief, however, the gap theory is based upon an inadmissible grammatical and philological treatment of the Hebrew text of Genesis 1:1–2 and receives little support from the remainder of Scripture.

One verse often quoted in its favour is Isaiah 45:18: 'For thus saith the LORD that created the heavens; God himself that formed the earth and made it; he hath established it, he created it not in vain [lit. a waste], he formed it to be inhabited.' Thus it is argued that the earth was not created in the state described in Genesis 1:2, but must

---

[18] W. W. Fields, *Unformed and unfilled* (see note 16, above).

have become waste at some subsequent time. However, this is surely a misunderstanding of both Isaiah and Genesis. The final clause of Isaiah's verse makes it clear that he is speaking of God's *intention*. He did not create the earth with the *purpose* of its being waste, but with the *purpose* that it would become inhabited. Genesis describes the earth as 'formless and void' only at an intermediate state in its development towards a completed, inhabitable condition, not in its final form. There is not the slightest conflict, therefore, between Isaiah and the traditional interpretation of Genesis 1:2.

As indicated earlier, the precise arguments for and against the gap theory turn on linguistic details in the Hebrew text and are too detailed to rehearse here. The present writer, however, would follow Fields in concluding that the theory is no more than a speculation born of the desire to fit geological time into a historical Genesis framework.

A variant of the gap theory is that a 'gap' or time expanse is implied *before* verse 1 of Genesis 1. To establish this idea it is necessary to read verse 1 as a conditional clause qualifying verse 2 (or perhaps verse 3): 'In the beginning of God's creating the heaven and the earth . . . the earth was without form and void.' The effect of this is (a) to produce an involved sentence quite at variance with the crisp style in which the remainder of the chapter is written, and (b) to expunge from Genesis 1 any reference to creation *ex nihilo*, a doctrine clearly taught elsewhere in Scripture (Heb. 11:3). For these reasons this theory has not attracted widespread support.

The third method of reconciliation will be mentioned here only in passing, namely that Genesis 1 merely describes the revelation to Adam, over a seven-day period, of the facts of creation.[19] According to this view, the six days do not refer to the time-period of creation at all, but only to the period of revelation. This engaging idea seems, however, to contradict flatly Exodus 20:11 ('In six days the LORD *made* . . .'), and also the plain meaning of such

---

[19] P. J. Wiseman, *Clues to Creation in Genesis* (London: Marshall, Morgan and Scott, 1977).

words as, 'On the seventh day God ended his work'. It is surely inadmissible to rewrite this verse: 'On the seventh day God ended the revelation of his work,' and yet such rewriting is necessitated by the theory in question.

To summarize, therefore, the various attempts to reconcile fully the geological time-scale with a historical interpretation of Genesis 1: all fail to rise above the level of speculation, and also all introduce interpretative problems at least as great as those they solve. Under these circumstances, and in the absence of further light on the matter, it would seem wise to accept that Genesis teaches a straightforward miraculous creation of earth and its biosphere in six days, each day being the earth's period of rotation on its own axis. It seems to the writer that the first day only may legitimately be extended backwards in time to encompass the original (and equally miraculous) creation of the universe and the 'formless' earth at some indefinitely prior time, though many creationists would argue that even this possibility is excluded by Exodus 20:11.

Is creation finished?

We have devoted considerable space to the first area of conflict between evolution and the Bible simply because the time-scale issue is the one to which most attention has been directed. It will be possible to deal with the remaining five areas much more concisely, not because they are less important, but simply because theistic evolution seems to offer very little to support its position in respect of these matters.

The completed nature of biblical creation is evident both from Genesis 2:2 ('God ended his work . . . and he rested on the seventh day from all his work which he had made') and from the past tense employed in John 1:3 and other Scriptures. At the same time the Bible maintains that God is ever active in *providence*, 'upholding all things by the word of his power' (Heb. 1:3, AV). Thus a clear distinction is drawn between a past, completed creation and a present, ongoing providence. Theistic evolution, however, maintains that God's creative work was executed by means of the ongoing evolutionary process which is still operative today. Thus creation is not yet complete, and providence cannot be clearly distinguished from creation. It seems extremely difficult to reconcile these concepts with the Bible's insistence that creation was fully completed at some past era.

Two possible arguments are available to theistic evolution. The first is that evolution may by asymptotic, that is, rapid at first but tending to a stationary condition so that the major part of all potential evolution has already occurred. In this sense creative evolution might be said to have exhausted its potential and be 'finished'. A second argument is similar but somewhat different, namely that evolution achieved its highest potential in the emergence of man and in that sense only can be held to have 'ended'. All subsequent (and thus current) evolution leads to elaboration and diversification of the biosphere without promoting it to any higher plane.

These arguments face two major difficulties. Firstly, of course, they side-step the plain implication of Scripture which says that God 'rested . . . from *all* his work'. This seems to be such a categorical statement of a fully finished creation as to leave no room for any kind of major subsequent diversification of life forms. The second problem is that these arguments contradict the basic tenet of evolutionary theory, namely that all past biological development occurred by natural processes observable today. If this were true, there is clearly no ground for saying that the future course of evolution will differ in any significant way from its past. If great changes have taken place in the past through the agencies of mutation and natural selection, then there is no reason why they should not continue to do so. In particular there is no basis for the idea that evolution has exhausted its potential or that it has, in man, yet spawned its 'highest possible achievement'. In reality, therefore, the arguments appeal to evolution *plus* its regulation by God in such a way that events occurred in the past which are prohibited today by divine intervention. But this undermines the fundamental uniformitarian concept that past evolution can be wholly explained by processes observable today. The biblical teaching of a finished creation seems to present insuperable difficulties, therefore, to a consistent doctrine of theistic evolution.

Evolution or degeneration?

As indicated earlier, evolution teaches a progressive 'upward' tendency while Scripture relates the story of a perfect creation which has undergone degeneration. How may this 'directional conflict' be resolved? Clearly, theistic evolution can subscribe to a moral and spiritual degeneracy on the part of mankind as a whole. What it cannot embrace, however, is a literal 'fall' of the first man Adam, since there was no such single man but only an evolving population which emerged from apehood into manhood. Neither can evolutionary thinking accept the idea that the fall of man led to a degeneracy in the natural order, as taught in Genesis 3 and Romans 8. It is very difficult to spiritualize away the contrast between the initial creation, which was 'very good', and the present natural order, 'subject to vanity' and in 'the bondage of corruption' described in Romans 8. Once again, therefore, a reconciliation between biblical doctrine and theistic evolution seems impossible.

It should perhaps be made clear at this point that the creationist view does not necessarily require that death was unknown in the animal and vegetable kingdoms before the fall, nor that the laws of physics underwent change at that time. For example, some suggest that the Second Law of Thermodynamics did not operate before the fall.[20] Clearly *some* forms of death and decay were intrinsic to the original creation of the 'tree yielding fruit, whose seed was in itself' (Gn. 1:12) since flower and fruit both decay before seed is released. Again such phenomena as friction (without which we could neither walk nor grip), and the elasticity of, for example, skin, derive from the Second Law of Thermodynamics! It is not necessary to make extravagent claims to fortify the biblical teaching that some fundamental change took place in the natural order, introducing suffering, disease and human death, and rendering nature subject to 'the bondage of corruption'. The point to grasp at this juncture, however, is that theistic evolution finds it very difficult to make room in

[20] H. M. Morris, *The Genesis record* (Welwyn: Evangelical Press, 1977), p. 127.

its uniformitarian scheme for the physical consequences of the spiritual fall of Adam, nor indeed for the deliverance and restoration of the natural order so clearly promised in the New Testament.

Creation, miraculous or natural?

Evolution can allow a single creative act, namely the origination from nothing of matter and energy. Intrinsic in this initial act is the creation also of space, time and natural law. From that moment onwards, however, the physical universe is supposed to have developed and evolved by the operation of physical law without the further intervention of divine fiat or creative activity. The creationist justifiably asks why further miraculous acts should be ruled out in respect of origins when theistic evolutionists allow that 'modern' miracles, such as the resurrection of Jesus Christ, have indeed taken place. Theistic evolution seems to be guided by philosophical principles which are wholly extra-biblical in so rigorously excluding any miraculous actions subsequent to the creation of energy and matter. The miraculous creation of life, for example, from existing inanimate chemicals ('dust') would seem a minor problem when set against the *ex nihilo* creation of matter itself.

The Genesis account of creation is most naturally interpreted as a succession of miraculous acts, each introduced by the words: 'And God said, Let . . .'. Of course, it is possible to maintain that this repeated expression simply records the various progressive stages of geological and biological evolution as they occurred. But if nothing is intended by these words other than a providential guiding of natural process, it is difficult to see why they are uniquely employed in the creation account and not on every other page of Scripture! The clear implication of such phrases as, 'Let there be . . . and there was', is that some event took place by the direct intent of God which *would not otherwise have happened* (that is, would not have occurred by natural process). If this were not the case it is difficult to see why such language should be used at all.

A compromise position known as 'progressive

creation'[21] has been proposed, which accepts that Genesis describes a succession of miraculous acts such as the creation of life and of the major types of living organism. These creative acts, however, are widely separated in time (day-age theory) and interspersed by periods of normal evolution within the major kinds. This idea has some similarities to the basic creationist view, for creationism allows for process to occur from the moment of creation and thus for miracle in one sphere to occur contemporaneously with process in another. Furthermore, creationists do not deny that processes of variation occur within the created kinds. Finally, progressive creation denies the essential evolutionary concept that all life has arisen from a single original life-form, itself the product of chance natural occurrences; but it allows for the geological time-scale within the six-day creation and thus maintains that the fossil record (with its implications of suffering, sudden death and catastrophe) was formed before the creation and fall of Adam. This is difficult to reconcile with the biblical teaching on the physical effects of the fall upon an originally perfect creation.

It is appropriate here to clarify the creationist position against a common misunderstanding. In contending that Genesis describes a succession of miraculous creative acts we do not eliminate process from the record. For one thing, of course, natural process must apply to a created object or life-form from the moment of its creation. 'The earth brought forth herb *yielding seed*.' The 'bringing forth' was miraculous, but the yielding of seed was the consequence of natural process. Similarly the created waters would have obeyed the laws of hydrodynamics and hydrostatics from the instant of creation, even *while* other miraculous works were being wrought within their depths, such as the creation of aquatic life. Secondly, process-in-time seems to have been involved in some of the creative acts themselves. Indeed the extension of creation over six days seems to require this. Thus the gathering together of the waters into seas (Gn. 1:9; Ps. 104:6–9) seems to have involved the flow of water under the influence of gravity

---

[21] B. Ramm, *op. cit.*, p. 76.

but, perhaps, at a miraculously reduced viscosity (that is, accelerated speed). We shall see later that no philosophical or theological problem arises from this intermingling of the miraculous with process. This is an important point, since many intellectual difficulties and entrenched positions in this debate arise from the problem of harmonizing miracle with nature in a single world-view.

Was evolution God's agency in creation?

We now come to the last of our six areas of conflict, namely the difficulty of reconciling a random amoral process like evolution with the purpose and tenderness attributed to God by the Bible in respect of the physical creation. That the worlds were created for a *purpose* is evident from Revelation 4:11: 'Thou art worthy, O Lord, to receive glory and honour and power: for thou hast created all things, and for thy pleasure they are and were created.' That the worlds were *designed* with intricate care is evident to all who believe in a Creator, both from the testimony of science and from Scripture itself (*e.g.* Pss. 139:14–16; 19:1; 8:3; 104:1–35; Ne. 9:6). That a tenderness characterizes God's attitude towards his created order is clear both from the Psalms already cited and the teachings of Christ himself ('Your heavenly Father feedeth [the fowls of the air]'; 'Are not two sparrows sold for a farthing? And one of them shall not fall . . . without your Father', Mt. 6:26; 10:29). Thus purpose and tenderness typify the relationship revealed in Scripture between the Creator and the creature. Evolution stands in such contrast to this picture that it is very difficult to envisage it as God's method of creation. Firstly, of course, evolution appeals to chance processes such as random genetic mutation involving at least ninety-nine *harmful* mutations to every one beneficial mutation. Evolution's 'experiments' therefore give rise to a vast potential for suffering in the animal kingdom for every 'upward' step towards a diversified biosphere. Again, the essential process of natural selection or the 'survival of the fittest' frequently (though not always) involves destructive competition between species. Even the balance of nature as observed today, with its food-chain involving the death of myriads of living creatures, must be an essential part of the evolutionary picture. In contrast the Bible implies that in the original creation only vegetable matter was to be used for food (Gn. 1:29–30; *cf*. Is. 11:6–9) and suggests that the necessity for animal foodstock (Gn. 9:3) arose after the fall and possibly only after the flood.

The biblical picture, then, is one in which the processes observed today (competition for survival, a carnivorous natural order and harmful genetic mutations) were not present in the 'good' creation as it came from the hand of God. These things, and other features of nature as we know it, arose subsequently as a result of the fall of man. God did not create the world in 'the bondage of corruption' but 'subjected' it to this condition as a result of Adam's disobedience. The 'whole creation' thus 'groaneth and travaileth in pain' awaiting the consummation of the gospel era and the return of Christ, when it will itself be delivered 'into the glorious liberty of the children of God' (Rom. 8:19–23, AV).

If this be the case, it is clear that the processes of neo-Darwinian evolution, *even if* they were shown to be capable today of transforming one species into another, could not have been responsible for the original work of creation. They reflect the consequences of sin rather than the character of the Creator, God's judgmental order rather than his creative means.

Creation and science: a synthesis

The reader might well ask, 'Having rejected theistic evolution, what alternative view of creation can you offer which is wholly consistent with the biblical record and with the facts of modern scientific observation?' It is my purpose in this final section to attempt to answer that question. I have suggested several times that one of the basic problems for many people is that of reconciling the miraculous with providence on the one hand and modern science on the other. I believe that theistic evolution, progressive creation and many of the ideas associated with these views are espoused by Christians, consciously or unconsciously, in an attempt to solve this basic dilemma. Consequently, our task of constructing a world-view which is both biblical and scientifically acceptable needs to begin with these basic matters rather than with the creation story.

A theology of science

I have suggested elsewhere the urgent need for a theological framework in which to set the methods and findings of modern science. Without such a 'theology of science', the conflict between science and religion remains both unresolved *and* ill-defined. Thus to understand better the past relationship between God and his created universe, we begin by examining their present relationship. In Colossians 1:15–19 we find this relationship defined. Of course, this is a *Christocentric* passage having as its main purpose the establishment of the coequality of Christ and the Father. But it is exactly this design on the part of the apostle which makes the passage so valuable for our purpose because in identifying the attributes of God shared by Christ, the writer cannot omit the question of the creation and sustenance of the material universe. 'By him [Christ]', declares Paul, 'were all things created, that are in heaven and that are in earth, visible and invisible . . . all things were created by him, and for him.' Thus the apostle repeats the assertions of the prologue to John's Gospel, concerning the agency in creation of the Second Person of the triune God. But Paul continues, 'And he is before all things, and by him all things consist.' This verse emphasizes Christ's precedence, both in time and status, over the whole created order, but it also states explicitly the dependent relationship that exists between him and the physical world. 'By him all things consist', that is, hold together. The integrity of the material realm is a derived integrity. It consists not so much in the intrinsic properties of matter and energy but in the present-tense being of the Deity.

In scientific terms, of course, we would say that 'all things hold together' by the operation of physical law, but we do not deceive ourselves into thinking that the laws of science are the efficacious *cause* of the integrity of nature. We recognize that the laws are simply our *description* of the manner in which the universe functions. The true *cause* of the forces and natural processes described by scientific law lies beyond the realm of scientific investigations. We do not, as scientists, speculate why masses attract one another, nor why the law of gravity is an inverse square law rather than, say, an inverse cube law. We simply accept nature as we find it, and attempt to describe its myriad phenomena in laws as few and as general as may be possible. In doing so we discover a mathematical harmony and order about creation that is positively aesthetic in its appeal, namely the element of 'design'. The fact that science reveals a category of order in nature that our *human minds are capable of appreciating* is, of course, evidence that creation is the product of an intelligence not wholly dissimilar to our own.

Returning to Colossians 1:17, then, we may conclude that scientific law is a description of the manner in which Christ upholds and sustains the natural order. We do not limit this work to the natural universe, since the context clearly embraces non-material entities among the 'all things' which consist in him. It is equally clear, however, that the physical creation is very much in the writer's mind as he identifies Christ as the source of all being.

Unlike creation, which is a past, accomplished work (Col. 1:16: 'were created'), the sustaining power of Christ is a present and continuous activity. This, moreover, is a more fundamental activity than that normally delineated by the term 'providence'. Providence is described elsewhere by the same apostle in these terms: 'All things work together for good to them that love God . . .' (Rom. 8:28). Of course, providence is not limited to the believer, and in that sense this verse does not define it fully, but the distinction I wish to draw is between the two clauses, 'all things consist' and 'all things work'. The first clause surely refers to the very *constitution* of things while the second refers to their *operation* or function. Thus God's employment of ravens to feed Elijah was providential; the fact that such things as ravens existed to be so employed is the burden of Colossians 1:17.

A second New Testament Scripture may now be cited to reinforce what we have stated so far, namely Hebrews 1:1–3. This passage is remarkably similar to Colossians

1:15–19, having the same Christological purpose, and identifying Christ as God's agent 'by whom also he made the worlds'. Verse 2 continues, 'Who being the brightness of [God's] glory, and the express image of his person, and upholding all things by the word of his power. . . .'

This last clause expresses in different words the same idea as Colossians 1:17, namely that 'all things' are upheld or sustained by the ever-present activity of God. An added thought appears in this verse, namely that Christ imparts integrity to the material universe by the 'word of his power'. Here lies the effectual cause of those material interactions and processes described and employed by science. The source of, say, the binding energy of the atom is the power of God. Material energy is derived from pure spiritual energy. This concept is necessary of course to account for the initial creation *ex nihilo*, but our verse suggests that God's spiritual power not only originated matter and energy, but sustains it in existence and controls its interactions and processes.

The full expression 'the word of his power' is surely intended to convey purpose or intention. He upholds all things not just by his power, but by a deliberate putting forth or exercise of that power. God is the *active* source of being, not just a passive 'ground of existence'. This adds new point to Paul's famous declaration that 'in him we live, and move, and have our being' (Acts 17:28). God is active, sentient, purposeful in his upholding and sustaining of the physical worlds. This final point is vital as we come now to examine the question of miracles.

Miracles

By definition, a miracle involves the supplanting of natural process and physical law. For the time required for the miracle to take place, rules other than the normal physical laws govern and control events. Thus Christ's first miracle, in which water was turned into wine, conceivably involved the transformation of some atoms of oxygen into atoms of carbon followed by the assembly of sugar and other large molecules. None of these nuclear or chemical transformations would have occurred naturally under the conditions prevailing, and they must therefore have taken place under rules unknown to science which temporarily prevailed over normal scientific law. (We do not here concern ourselves with 'miracles of timing' in which natural processes are used by God to realize his purposes. Such miracles really fall under the heading of providence rather than the miraculous.)

Now we have maintained earlier that the normal laws of physics and chemistry are the moment-by-moment expression of God's will, the ever-present 'word of his power', the contemporaneous expression of his purpose. If this is so, the suspension or replacement of those laws becomes a very straightforward matter. God simply changes his 'instructions' to nature in such a manner and for such a period as is required for the miracle to be performed. Thus if the normal laws of physics require that oxygen atoms are stable and do not decay spontaneously into carbon atoms, such spontaneous decay, without release of catastrophic energy, may be brought about by a momentary change in the rules governing the stability of oxygen atoms. Since the normal rules are simply the present-tense expression of God's will, the extraordinary rules which momentarily supervene are also of this same nature. No inconsistency arises in God's mind or action; there is no arbitrary 'intervention' by God into the natural order; miracles are not amoral.

Creation

Let us now, as briefly as possible, apply these ideas to creation and providence. This we will do in outline only and the reader is referred elsewhere for a fuller statement.[22]

The *ex nihilo* creation, a concept unique to the Judaeo-Christian tradition, was an event in which matter and energy, space and time, together with the laws or principles that describe the structure and behaviour of these entities, were inaugurated from a purely spiritual source. Following this event, and in a period which is not necessarily limited by Scripture, the heaven and earth (that is, the whole universe) were formed. At some juncture the earth is recorded as existing 'without form and void'.

---

[22] E. H. Andrews, *From nothing to nature*.

Although miracle was obviously necessary for the origin of energy and matter, we accept that subsequent events leading to the 'formless' earth may have occurred by miracle, natural process or an admixture of the two, since Scripture gives us no certain guidance on this matter. The scene from this point in the creation narrative is earth itself.

Space will not permit us here to rehearse the details of the creation week. We take the view, however, that each repetition of the words: 'And God said. . .' introduces a new miraculous fiat in which events occurred which required the suspension or replacement of natural law. This applies not only to the obviously miraculous assembly of atoms and molecules (dust) into living organisms of various kinds, but also to events which could conceivably have happened by natural process. Thus the first light on earth *could* have dawned by the clearing of a dense atmosphere, by completely natural means. It could equally have appeared as a result of a *miraculous* clearing of such an atmosphere. This second alternative is just as much a miracle as that involved in the idea that Genesis 1:3 describes the first creation of light anywhere in the universe.

The miraculous creation of man is attested by two distinct arguments. Genesis 2:7 states that God formed man directly from the 'dust' in the same manner as he formed the animals. This seems to exclude the formation of Adam from *already viable species*. Furthermore, the second half of the same verse indicates that a special act of vivification was required ('man became a living soul': by common consent, 'soul' does not signify a spiritual dimension but simply a living organism). Such vitalization would be quite unnecessary had Adam evolved from existing primates. Secondly, whatever one makes of the account of woman's creation from one of Adam's 'sides', the New Testament explains that there was a temporal order in their creation ('Adam was first formed, then Eve', 1 Tim. 2:13). This again excludes the evolutionary transformation of an existing population of apes into *Homo sapiens*, since man and woman would then have necessarily evolved simultaneously.

Providence

The subject of providence has arisen several times in the course of this essay. We saw that theistic evolution blurs the distinction between creation and providence and is also inconsistent in that it regards providence as the same thing as God's supposed use of evolution as a creative agency. Providence is distinct from miracle in that it involves no suspension or replacement of natural process, but rather the use of such process to achieve particular aims.

The subject of providence is a large one, both biblically and philosophically. It involves questions of the sovereignty of God in human affairs, the permitted occurrence of evil and suffering and the matter of free will and determinism. It is not therefore a subject that can be developed here except to emphasize the very real differences between providence and creation which are confused or ignored by theistic evolution.

Of course, there is a continuity between creation and providence, as illustrated in Psalm 104 where a poetic account of creation (verses 1–9) passes naturally into a hymn of praise to God for his providential care over the things created. Did God create the grass and the herb? Then also he 'causeth the grass to grow for the cattle, and herb for the service of man' (verse 14). Did he create the dry land? Then also 'the high hills are a refuge for the wild goats; and the rocks for the conies' (verse 18). Nevertheless, in spite of this obvious continuity, the Bible's distinction between a past, completed creation (Gn. 2:1–2; Jb. 38:4; Ps. 104:5; Jn. 1:1–3; Heb. 1:2) and a present continuing providence is too self-evident to avoid. It is not possible, therefore, to ascribe 'creation' to providence, for the former involves the miraculous while the latter does not. To attribute creation to the overruling or direction of statistically determined events (which is an alternative definition of providence) is to apply the doctrine of uniformitarianism to the realm of God's activities, that is, to claim that God always acted in the past as he acts in the present. This is palpably unbiblical, for the progressive nature of God's dealings with the world and the human race, involving a miraculous origin and an equally miraculous culmination (for example, the resurrection of the dead) are undeniable if we believe the Bible at all.

Conclusion

Let us finally, therefore, draw together the threads of this discussion. We have argued against evolution on biblical grounds, citing six areas of conflict between the scriptural and evolutionary accounts of creation. These areas concerned the questions of time-scale, the finished nature of creation, the fall and its physical consequences, the plurality of the creative fiats, the inadequacy of natural process to account for the origin of the biosphere, and the moral problems associated with the idea of evolution as an agency of divine creation. We then moved on to discuss the philosophical shortcomings of evolution. We saw that, at best, it is a scientific hypothesis and that many of its assertions are, in fact, philosophical rather than scientific, being based on axioms rather than observations. Finally, we have seen that the Bible itself provides us with a key to the understanding of science and miracles, and that, using this key, we are able to accept the obvious historical interpretation of the Genesis creation story without doing violence to a proper view of science and natural process.

Perhaps the most important point we have argued is that Christians must adopt a biblical view of science and process and not borrow from extra-biblical philosophy a theory of science which rigorously excludes such biblical ingredients as the occurrence of miracles and the subjection of natural process to the will of God. These ideas have been developed in detail elsewhere.[23] If we were more robustly scriptural in our evaluation of science, we would be less inclined to be mesmerized by the tenuous logic, circular reasoning and leaps of faith which characterize the general theory of evolution.

[23] E. H. Andrews, *God, Science and Evolution* (Welwyn: Evangelical Press, 1980).

Response to E.H.Andrews

D. G. Jones

I find myself in a paradoxical position. I agree with much that Professor Andrews has written, especially on the most important issues. These I consider are found in the section 'Creation and science: a synthesis'. Oddly, though, that same section says little about evolution. This is probably because Professor Andrews is there speaking theologically, in an area on which there is a large measure of agreement between us. This is a crucial point, because it is all too easy to read our respective articles and conclude that we are poles apart as Christians. Such a conclusion would be grossly misleading. Why, then, are our views on the creation-evolution issue apparently so dissimilar?

Expectations of science
An answer to this question depends on our expectations of science and on the interrelationship of science and the Bible. I suggest that the different expectations are probably found only in the biological sciences; Professor Andrews is a physical scientist and it seems that the sorts of demands he makes on the biological sciences are not being made on the physical sciences.

It may be argued, of course, that, as a biological scientist, I have already compromised my position (and my faith). This I would resolutely deny. Biological science is as rigorously scientific as anything in physical science;

even the historical sciences are seriously scientific. On the biblical front I argue that the approach I adopt fits legitimately within an orthodox framework of biblical interpretation. I also contend that my approach is in line with that adopted by many of a reformed theological outlook, including Calvin and Warfield.

My approach diverges from that of Professor Andrews at the fundamental level of methodology. He espouses a biblicist view of historical biology. He insists on employing biblical ideas within biological science. The consequence of this is that biological science becomes methodologically inseparable from theology. To many Christians this may sound the ideal way in which science should be tackled. After all, it appears to place science within a biblical framework and to give it a biblical base. The directions are Christian ones; the details can be left to the scientist.

Is this 'Christian biology', and is it what we have all been waiting for? I imagine that Professor Andrews may reply 'Yes'. Before rushing headlong in this seemingly enticing direction, however, we should ask what other examples of Christian science there may be: Christian nuclear physics? Christian materials science? Christian radiology? Perhaps even a Christian motor car?

In posing these questions I do not have in mind the philosophical background to these sciences, nor the attitudes with which practitioners of the sciences approach their disciplines. At these levels, there are specifically Christian contributions to every science; to every activity in fact. What I do have in mind is a specifically Christian contribution which actually alters the way in which we *do* the scientific work. This is what I take Professor Andrews to mean. The biology Christians carry out should, according to him, be different from that of non-Christians, because Christians are provided with perceptions and principles that control what they can think *as biologists*. If this is the case with biology, is it also the case with the other pure and applied sciences? If so, what are the relevant biblical principles in those areas?

Response to E. H. Andrews

A Christian biology

If there is such a phenomenon as Christian biology, what are the principles on which it is based? Professor Andrews appears to argue that such principles are found mainly in Genesis 1. For these principles to be binding on all Christians, they must be seen to be unequivocally Christian – in other words, they must be so clearly taught in the Bible that they cannot be denied.

Professor Andrews devotes much of his article to an attempt to demonstrate just this. I submit that the fact that he goes to very great lengths to justify his interpretation of the details of Genesis 1 disproves that the principles he advocates are binding on all Christians. The 'days' of Genesis 1 may be 24-hour periods, they may be chronological, they may have existed 10,000 years ago; Adam may have been a historical person in *precisely* the same way as Abraham was a historical person. These are legitimate theological positions to hold. The crucial issue, however, is whether the biblical teaching is *so clear* that all Christians with a high view of Scripture are *obliged* to adopt these particular viewpoints.

Professor Andrews believes the interpretations he has put forward are correct. There is, and has been for many years, divergence of opinion on these matters within evangelical theological circles – a divergence due to the nature of the biblical evidence itself rather than to the faithfulness or unfaithfulness of the theologians.

It is no longer just an issue of theological niceties – important as that is. The interpretation of Genesis 1 advocated by Professor Andrews has been made the basis of biological science. It is no longer enough for Christians to agree on the major doctrine of God as Creator. They must now agree on the specific mechanisms by which God created, mechanisms that follow from a particular interpretation of Genesis 1 and 2. Those Christians who do not agree with the interpretation put forward by Professor Andrews will end up with a different basis for biological science.

Evangelical Christians, therefore, are being forced into opposing *scientific* camps because they do not see eye-to-eye over aspects of biblical interpretation. But how can

Professor Andrews be *absolutely sure* that all facets of his approach to Genesis 1 and 2 are correct? For biblical scholars this is a difficult area, especially as it is dealing with the question of origins. These are not simple black-and-white matters. Should we expect a simple answer in such a profound and complex area?

I do not believe we should, and I certainly cannot see that any *one* interpretation of these passages of Scripture *is so assured* that it demands of us its acceptance *in all its details*. Yet this is what is here required of us. This is an astonishing demand, when evangelical Christians cannot agree on all details of baptism, church government, the charismata, the ordination of women, or divorce. These are just as important, and one might say relatively easy, issues compared with the conundrum of precisely how God brought the world and all living creatures into existence. Why, then, expect complete agreement on points of inordinate difficulty, while allowing the coexistence of divergent viewpoints on matters of everyday practical concern?

And what about non-Christians? I imagine we do not expect to convince non-Christians of the correctness of a particular biblical interpretation. Does this mean that the biological science practised by non-Christians will inevitably differ from that allegedly practised by one group of evangelical Christians? The answer must be 'Yes', since there is no scientific reason why non-Christians should take as the basis for their science the book of Genesis.

The special creationist response to all this is to attempt to convince the world of the deficiencies of evolutionary thinking, and to argue either that special creation is a scientific concept (as in the USA); or that there are other scientific explanations of the data. Professor Andrews adopts the *scientific* hypothesis known as 'flood geology'. So far, very few non-Christians (or Christians) have been convinced. To most people, this response by the special creationist is not science at all, but simply one reading of Genesis 1.

Response to E. H. Andrews

Theistic evolution

A major difficulty I have with Professor Andrews' article is his classification of Christian attitudes into just two types – creationist and theistic evolutionist. This is a great over-simplification. As I have argued in my article, all biblical Christians must, by definition, be creationists. He should use the term 'special creationist' where he is implying a particular mechanism of creation.

Professor Andrews infers that the only alternative to such special creationism is theistic evolutionism. I believe that in saying this he sets up a straw-man – theistic evolution – which he then proceeds to knock down. This is misleading. The concept of theistic evolution is not a particularly fashionable one today, and there are few who hold this view. Yet he summarily dismisses complementarity at the beginning of the article, a far more popular, and I would suggest serious, contemporary position than theistic evolutionism. Progressive creationism also receives rather unsympathetic treatment. This is unfortunate, as it represents a provocative compromise stance within evangelicalism.

Probably all evangelical Christians, including myself, would unhesitatingly call themselves creationists. This is what we are theologically. Further, I have no stake in advocating a 'consistent doctrine of theistic evolution', but as one of Christ's people in a secular world, my task is to respond to that world as a biblically-oriented, biological scientist. This is not compromise; it is commitment.

Science and chance

Professor Andrews finds difficulty in 'reconciling a random amoral process like evolution with the purpose and tenderness attributed to God by the Bible in respect of the physical creation'. This raises two issues. The first concerns the nature of scientific explanation, which is always, by definition, amoral. Scientific descriptions never take account of morality. They are purposely framed in objective neutral terms. Hence evolutionary descriptions must be the same. There is therefore no difficulty from a Christian angle.

A scientific description of the digestive processes will be

257

amoral. What happens to food once it has been eaten has no moral overtones, even if it was human flesh that was eaten. The morality comes in the human intention concerning what is to be eaten, not in the description of the processes themselves. A description and understanding of the human intention are not the province of science.

It is for this reason that 'creation versus evolution' approaches are misleading. Creation refers to God and his purposes; evolution to a description of how things came to be as they are now, in terms of scientifically-based processes. Whether or not evolutionary mechanisms are correct, partially correct, or wrong is a matter for science – not for Christians as Christians. To pit God against a set of scientific descriptions of a process is at best meaningless, and at worst a denigration of the character of God.

Another aspect of this confusion of levels of understanding is the repeated criticism of evolutionary ideas on the grounds that they depend upon 'chance processes'. God does not use chance, so the argument goes; he is a purposeful God. What is overlooked is that, in evolutionary schemes, as in science generally, chance is used in a technical sense and not in a theological sense.

To refer to chance processes in science is not to deny the hand of God in an event. It may simply reflect our ignorance of underlying mechanisms, or it may have specific mathematical connotations. When speaking scientifically, the opposite of chance is neither purpose nor God (because these are foreign to scientific terminology), but known scientific causes.

Repeatedly we have to hold chance processes (in a scientific sense) and God's purposes (in a theological sense) together. The creation-evolution debate provides just one example of this. Another example in biology is the development of individual foetuses. Fertilization of a sperm and ovum, and the genetic constitution of the resulting foetus, are supreme examples of chance processes. Each one of us is a unique individual because of a host of chance events. This is a scientific statement, not a theological one. God's purposes can be seen in retrospect, as we look back and recognize his care and concern for us in the womb, and his plans for us throughout eternity; but it is possible to talk meaningfully and helpfully about the 'chance' of having a second mongol child. We have to face the fact that God is working his purposes out today, and he does so through chance events.

Conclusion

I do not agree with Professor Andrews that there are arguments against evolution on biblical grounds. This is akin to saying that there are biblical arguments against relativity, or the quantum theory, or the vesicle hypothesis in neurobiology. I do not believe there are biblical arguments either for or against such ideas. By contrast, biblical principles are highly relevant in arguing against the *use* (that is, the mis-use) of evolutionary ideas in supporting the political aspirations of one racial group against another, just as they are very relevant when considering abortion or apartheid.

Professor Andrews has been at great pains to disown the idea that evolution is an agency of divine creation. In this, I have sympathy with him, not because I agree with his arguments but because this mixture of scientific and theological levels of understanding is a confusion of terms. However, I feel that Professor Andrews is asking too much of theology. It is one thing to think, as did theologians of the past, that theology is the queen of sciences. It is another to suggest that theology replaces science – at least certain areas of the biological sciences. To me, this is a philosophical error.

My disagreement with Professor Andrews is therefore a philosophical one. This is an important point to realize because it may enable us and those Christians we each represent to appreciate where we go from here. So often, the disagreement is framed in theological terms, and the ensuing debate centres around our respective faithfulness in adhering to biblical revelation. This is a mistake; more often in orthodox theological circles the point of departure is a philosophical one.

To get anywhere in the creation-evolution debate, new attitudes are needed. Proving or disproving the factuality of evolution will get nowhere; justifying one interpretation of Genesis 1 over another will not help, unless there are

new insights yet to come from the Bible. To realize that
we differ over what science, especially biological science,
is all about, and the implications of this for Christian
thinking, is the only road to reconciliation. Perhaps it will
even lead to some original and creative thinking.

9
Summary and conclusion

O. R. Barclay

I have been asked to try to bring the discussion to some sort of summary and conclusion. It would be wrong to pretend that there is agreement about some of the major issues, but it would be equally wrong to suggest that the disagreements are as fundamental as is often said.

It is a pity that many of the authors did not address themselves specifically to the 'Theses' printed at the beginning. If they had done so the areas of agreement or disagreement might have been a little more clearly defined. But it is not difficult to identify the issues and I shall do so in terms of the Theses that were originally put forward.

Agreements

There is unqualified agreement about Theses 1 and 2: that God is the sovereign Creator of all things, that he created *ex nihilo*, and whereas the whole of creation was 'very good', man is not very good. He is a fallen being, sinful and not improving morally by any evolutionary process. There is no built-in process of moral improvement in God's world and all our authors are in unqualified opposition to the attempts to derive a philosophy of progress from science or a reduction of man's sin to anything less than rebellion against God. Sin is not a relic of animal ancestry. All the authors are agreed about the gospel and

261

O. R. Barclay

Dr Gish's fear that adopting a theistic evolutionary position will lead to the abandonment of the fundamentals of the Christian message would be strenuously denied by the authors on the theistic evolutionary side of the debate.

Disagreements

Beyond that point there are three main areas of disagreement. These all concern the *method of creation.*

A. General issues

Entropy and vestiges
Dr Gish uses the argument from entropy. Professor Burke believes that it is logically invalid. On the other side (although it comes under *B.* below) Professor Wright argues that the evidence for evolution from vestiges is invalid and none of our authors defends it. Probably both arguments should be dropped from the general debate, as they indeed have been by many. Many special creationist authors (in future S C for short) would not want to use the entropy argument (except possibly in a far more sophisticated form) and most theistic evolution authors (T E for short) would not want to argue from vestiges. Although they may themselves think that there is some force in the arguments and that they are worth further study, they see that they do not convince others. A bad argument is worse than silence.

Evolutionary philosophies
Dr Gish and Professor Andrews argue that the adoption of an evolutionary view of origins has in fact led to some blatantly anti-Christian philosophies and moral tendencies. The T E authors agree that the evolutionary philosophies are heretical and destructive (see Thesis 1), but do not believe that they have any necessary or valid connection with the scientific theories. They believe that the writers concerned have simply tried to use the prestige of science to boost their views, which would otherwise seem to have no good basis. They do not believe that evolution leads to evolutionism (any more than relativity leads to relativism).

262

Death

None of our authors feels it necessary to refute Thesis 6 about death in animals (not man). If that is agreed, or is regarded as too insecure a point, then some of the popular discussion of this issue can be set on one side. See, however, the next point.

Ethical issues

Dr Gish finds the whole process of large-scale evolution ethically unacceptable (he does not therefore accept the last part of Thesis 7). He did not have an opportunity of replying to the charge that in that case he must justify the very large number of species that have become extinct and the vast numbers of animals that are eaten each day by other animals. He must refute the accusation that he has given away too much to the atheists, who find both equally unacceptable. If it is agreed (and see his reply, p. 192) that natural selection does take place in God's world, even on a very *small* scale, then we must be careful to cover ourselves more than has been done here before we say that evolution is ethically unacceptable and therefore unbelievable as a process in creation on a *large* scale. All our authors of course accept that we are now talking about a fallen world that is not perfect. The S C authors argue that what is ethically acceptable in a fallen world as a part of providence would be ethically unacceptable as a process in a perfectly good creation. If God uses natural selection now, however, that takes some of the force out of the argument that it is ethically unacceptable.

Miracle and process

Thesis 3 stated that 'we cannot say that God's sovereign acts are always sudden and without process. Events of nature represent God's sovereignty whether they are subject to scientific explanation or not'. Here there is a difference of emphasis on the two sides of the debate. Probably none of our authors would disagree with the thesis as so stated. All our authors accept that God upholds all things and that he rules the world in loving providence. Professor Andrews, Professor Wright and Dr Gish, however, do think of sudden and scientifically inexplicable events as in some sense more fitting and more in keeping with the biblical record for the process of creation, than a long process which could be described in scientific terms.

Here we are up against differences that go wider than evolution. They affect our view of miracles and our view of how God works in the world today and how he answers prayer, *etc*. Those who see God's hand mainly or entirely in scientifically inexplicable events will naturally tend to side with the anti-evolutionists. Those who see God's hand equally in his providence and in his processes in history and in nature would have more sympathy with those who believe that God took a long time to create things. They will not feel the force of those arguments against evolution which depend on the view that a sudden inexplicable process is more likely from the standpoint of faith. This is not a simple question, but the S C authors make a far sharper distinction than the T E authors between miracle and providence, and see no difficulty in suggesting that a large number of special miracles, in addition to those mentioned in the Bible, were associated with both the creation and the flood (see also Dr Andrews' reply to Dr Fraser, p. 45).

B. Scientific issues

Theses 6–11 refer to the scientific issues discussed at length in this book. There are difficulties of a *scientific* kind in maintaining both a T E and S C position.

There are scientific difficulties in holding an evolutionary view, and they become greater as the scale of evolution increases. None of our writers doubts that there has been some change of an adaptative nature as our environment has changed. There are, it is agreed, well documented cases of hereditary changes arising in artificial selection and some in natural selection. Those that can be documented are all inevitably of a fairly short time-scale, and represent small changes (changes with melanic varieties of moths in the 'Black Country' is a good example). The disagreement is about whether such changes based upon such mechanisms can explain large-scale changes also. The S C authors maintain that the evidence for large-scale changes is weak and that the mechanisms that are adequate for small-scale change cannot explain large-scale changes also. In this they take sides in a scientific debate that is still going on. Most T E authors would say that even if exactly the same small-scale mechanisms are not sufficient mechanisms for large-scale change, the evidence of large-scale changes taking place remains. It is the job of science to discover, if it can, what mechanisms were involved – whether or not they see the hand of God in those mechanisms. The fact that there is still some debate about the mechanisms by which change took place does not in itself affect the evidence which suggests that those changes did take place. It is dangerous to invoke God just when there is something you think you cannot understand scientifically. If the changes took place at all, and over a long period of time, then we expect to find scientific processes – controlled, of course, as all scientific and chance processes are, by God.

Large-scale changes seem to need enormously long time, so the debate has come in considerable measure to focus on the question of the age of the earth and the meaning of the word 'day' in Genesis 1.

The T E writers believe that there is overwhelming evidence that the earth is very old and that large-scale evolution has taken place. The S C writers believe that although some of the evidence may be most naturally interpreted in that way, another (short time-scale) explanation is at least equally convincing. They hold that the scientific difficulties of evolution, some of which they set out, are formidable and are if anything getting worse as time passes and further discoveries are made.

If there are scientific difficulties about maintaining a T E view, there are also *scientific difficulties about maintaining an S C view*. Professor Burke mentioned some of them, and the S C authors do not here explain fully how they solve the problems. They concentrated on criticisms of evolution and did not set out fully their alternative explanations of the scientific phenomena. Had they had space, they would no doubt have addressed that question more fully.

The S C writers must accept '*an apparent age*' view in at least a very limited way. Adam on Day 6 would have appeared to be, say, 20 years old. The trees would have appeared to be older. Stars would have appeared to a scientific mind to be millions of years old (because millions of light-years away). Let us say that an observer on Day 1 would have seen a scientific age for these things, even though the time necessary for that age had in fact never taken place. In so far as the S C authors accept apparent age they accept, as the word 'apparent' implies, that *scientifically* the world appears to be much older than they say that it is. The S C writers, therefore, have to choose between two explanations and the difficulties in the two cases are different. They could, firstly, decide for a very limited apparent age (which would not now leave many scientific traces because it was so limited) coupled with a sudden creation at a relatively recent date (for which they find some scientific evidence). Alternatively, they could decide for a wholesale apparent age that explains all those scientific phenomena that cannot easily be explained in terms of a recent creation. Professor Andrews' position combines some apparent age (mature creation) with many special miracles (see pp. 63ff.). Most S C writers would probably agree with this nowadays and reject wholesale apparent age as creating unacceptable delusions. They argue instead that most of the relevant phenomena of science can be scientifically explained in terms of a recent creation, if some process rates were (sometimes miraculously) very different from today. Here we come to the arguments put forward by Dr Fraser in geology and Professor Andrews' arguments on the other side. Obviously, a fuller discussion of the scientific issues on both sides could have been carried out, but it is not clear that that would have taken us much further.

C. *The interpretation of Genesis 1*

The interpretation of Genesis 1 (Theses 4 and 5) is probably the key area of disagreement and this raises wider issues. Professor Wright is certain that Genesis 1 is history. Professor Burke believes that it is likely to be symbolic as is the account of the end of the world in the book of Revelation. It seems that all our authors are agreed that Adam and Eve are the historical first parents of mankind who fell into sin at a historical time. If they do not believe that (and Professor Berry's position may be different) they certainly do not wish to dispute it. They regard it as perfectly compatible with a T E view of origins. There are many people on both sides of the debate who hold strongly to the historicity of Adam and Eve (because of the way that they are spoken about in the New Testament), who nevertheless have a fairly open mind about how Genesis 1 should be understood.

While it is agreed that Genesis 3 has clear historical content, there would not necessarily be agreement as to the kind of history it represents – that is to say the degree of literalness of all the details such as the tree of life and the curse, *etc.* That issue has not been discussed much in these pages because the key issue is Genesis 1 and not Genesis 2 and 3. There is much more agreement about Genesis 2 and 3 than about Genesis 1. Professor Andrews, however, argues that the debate is far wider than Genesis 1 (see the section in his paper where he discusses allegory and history).

Professor Wright points out that it is dangerous to treat Genesis 1 as 'symbolical', because this may easily lead to taking Genesis 2 and 3 as non-historical. He is correct. This has often happened; but that is not in itself a reason for refusing to adopt a position if it is thought to be true. People have said the same about the book of Revelation and described all who do not accept a very literal interpretation as crypto-liberals. The problem is to decide the literary form of each chapter and then to decide which phrases are to be understood literally and which are metaphors, *etc.*

The discussion under this heading is complex. The S C authors argue that Genesis 1 must be understood as history and also believe it is very dangerous to depart from a largely literal interpretation of Genesis 1 to 3 because this can and often has escalated into (or arisen from a previously accepted?) liberal position. On the T E side, our authors see no need for such escalation if we keep to the principle of the authority of Scripture and allow that which is plain in Scripture to interpret that which is not plain. They are not sure that phrases like 'the day' in Genesis 1 must be understood literally, nor do they believe that you can be dogmatic as to the range of meaning of the word 'kinds' or the different words for 'created' and 'made'. Others believe that we can and must treat them in a narrowly defined sense.

It does appear that the crux of the whole matter is in the question of how Genesis 1 should be understood. If it were not for strongly-held views about this, it is doubtful whether the whole debate would be particularly important. Genesis 1 bears on many other doctrines. Some of the staunchest defenders of biblical orthodoxy believe that, but still do not have a real problem here, because they do not think Genesis 1 should be understood as literally as most S C people believe it must.

A third option

Professor Jones cuts across the debate about evolution by proposing (most concisely in his reply to Professor Andrews) that the real issue is not creation by evolution (T E) or special creation at a recent date (S C). The real question is about how far Genesis 1 is meant to give us scientific data. On his view it is not an either/or question (S C or T E), but an open-or-shut question. Does the Bible intend to close these scientific issues? He believes not, and that we should allow room for several possibilities. The Bible may intend to leave as open questions the method and time-scale of creation. Scientists may agree or disagree on their answers, and theories may rise and fall without our being wedded to any of them. If, as Professor Andrews believes (and probably also the other S C writers), the alternative to T E is 'flood geology', then Professor Jones would not wish to be committed to either. Both are scientific views that have no biblical status.

We are able to summarize the whole situation as follows:

The most natural reading of the scientific data is, in the view of most scientists, in terms of a great age for the universe and for the earth. Most devout scientists who are in these fields find themselves compelled to accept that position. They find the scientific arguments for a young earth quite unconvincing. They think that those who reject the old earth view have never felt the full force of the facts in the relevant fields. Those who adopt the young earth point of view, however, feel that the biologists *etc.* have been brainwashed by the current orthodoxy in those fields and need to be helped to see the scientific data in a new way and to accept miracles as the explanation of the apparent age features.

Secondly, most of those who adopt the S C view and believe in a young earth go on to accept that the earth may be up to at least 10,000 years old. That is to say that they do not accept a strictly literal understanding of all the data in Scripture (which would bring the creation to less than 6,000 years ago and the flood to less than 5,000 years ago). Most of them also argue that geological phenomena (but not phenomena in most other sciences) are explained by the great flood. The so-called 'flood geology' has not been argued in detail here and has some of its own problems of consistency like every other theory. It is, however, hard to think of any other solution for the young earth advocates. They argue that natural processes must have been exceptionally speeded-up or slowed-down at the time of the creation and flood by the miraculous intervention of God, so that what might imply great age was in fact accomplished in a short space of time. Accepting that 'apparent age' is not the answer to everything, they believe that fast rates of sedimentation, mountain formation, fossilization, *etc.* can explain many of the phenomena and that the great flood is the supreme example of this of which we have clear biblical evidence. Here the young earth advocate usually feels that others do not give enough place to miracle, while the others usually feel that the young earth advocate invokes miracle too easily to solve difficulties which are better solved in scientific terms by an old earth view.

At the same time, many on both sides of the discussion will agree that *the most natural reading of Genesis 1 is in terms of creation in six 24-hour periods.* That, after all, is how it has normally been understood in the history of the church until quite recently. There are exceptions, like Augustine who thought it referred to a long process, and he had considerable influence; but at least since the seventeenth century most people have understood it in terms of six periods of 24 hours, until modern geology got going in the early nineteeth century (before Darwin). Therefore, as the last part of Thesis 11 says, the question of the interpretation of Genesis 1 is the crucial issue. Not many people would maintain the young earth position if they did not believe that Genesis 1 teaches it. They might be very critical of evolution, as some Marxists and others are, but they would be unlikely to support a young earth view unless they believed the doctrine of biblical authority required it.

The old earth advocates reply that firstly, if you concede that the earth may be older than 4004 BC, then the principle of literal interpretation has been abandoned and that it cannot in any case in their view be maintained with total consistency. Secondly, they say that we cannot shut our eyes to scientific evidence when we try to decide which parts of Scripture are to be understood literally and which are not. The young earth advocates would be inclined to say that this is to put science above Scripture. The old earth advocates would say that it is only to put all the knowledge we have at our disposal to try to understand the Bible correctly. They argue that it is science that has taught us to think of phrases like 'the four corners of the earth' and 'the windows of heaven' as non-literal and to accept that Psalm 93:1, which was so much disputed in the past, is not to be understood as a scientific statement ('the world is established; it shall never be moved'). They say that even if a strictly literal reading of Genesis 1 is the most natural (as it is for Ps. 93:1), we have to say that it is not the best way to read it. It was a mistake to allow our understanding of the Psalms to determine a scientific question. Are we in danger of a similar mistake over Genesis 1? Reading Genesis 1 either way, we want to be as careful as possible that we are being honest with what it actually teaches. But if even many of the S C advocates do not treat it *entirely* literally, then why should we be held to a *largely* literal reading when the evidence of God's created order is against it?

The S C advocates reply that the facts are not really against it; a young earth view is perfectly tenable. Also, if you are to know ideas by their fruits then you will adopt any evolutionary position however 'theistic' with extreme caution. The idea of 'evolution' does seem to be used to much philosophical mischief and they doubt whether that can be avoided by talking about God's control of the process.

There are, therefore, four interlocking questions:

1. How should Genesis 1 be rightly understood?
2. How should the scientific evidence be rightly understood?
3. How far can we use our understanding of science to help us to determine the right meaning of Scripture and vice versa?
4. Are there general considerations such as the incompatability of natural selection with God's perfect creation, or likely philosophical consequences of believing in biological evolution which push us into adopting one or other position?

I have suggested that the last type of argument is likely to be quite inconclusive. The disagreements in the first three areas remain, and hopefully this book will go some way to clarifying people's minds as to what position they ought to adopt.

About the contributors

Derek Burke, formerly Professor of Biological Sciences at Warwick University, is now Scientific Director and Vice-President of Allelix Inc. of Ontario, Canada.

E. H. Andrews is Professor of Materials Science, Queen Mary College, University of London.

Oliver R. Barclay, the editor of the When Christians Disagree series, was formerly General Secretary of the Universities and Colleges Christian Fellowship.

R. J. Berry is Professor of Genetics at University College London.

A. G. Fraser is Lecturer in Geology in the University of Hull, England.

Duane T. Gish is Associate Director of the Institute for Creation Research, El Cajon, California.

D. Gareth Jones is Professor of Anatomy in the University of Otago, New Zealand.

Verna Wright is Professor of Rheumatology in the University of Leeds.

Index of biblical references

To make this index as useful as possible, and to reflect the authors'
use of biblical passages as accurately as possible, all verse-group-
ings are indexed separately: for example, Genesis 2:1–2 and
Genesis 2:1–3 are not combined into a single entry. References
in **bold type** are to whole chapters rather than individual verses.

General index

Aaron's rod   37f.
Abraham   183, 231, 255
Adam: and the revelation
　　of creation   238
　antiquity of   15, 184
　as ancestor of
　　mankind   14, 168,
　　172f.
　as historical figure   99ff.,
　　140, 164, 186, 191,
　　231ff., 255, 267;
　　see also Scripture,
　　interpretation of
　his offspring   101, 114
　his sin   93, 105, 130;
　　see also fall, the
　in the creation of Eve   65,
　　140, 250
Agassiz, L.   212
age of the earth   15, 17–75,
　　103, 165, 173f., 183ff.,
　　193f., 216, 234ff.,
　　265ff.; see also apparent
　　age; flood geology
Ager, D.   154f.
Alps   22ff., 31, 43

amino acid sequences   135,
　　175ff., 189
ancestor   14, 29, 100ff.,
　　152f., 232; see also
　　transitional forms
Antarctic   21
anti-evolutionism
　　See creationism
apparent age   15, 36ff.,
　　173f., 184ff., 216, 266ff.
Archaeopteryx   94, 153f.
Armstrong, B. L.   60
Arran island   72
Asimov, I.   145n.
Auerbach, C.   92n.
Augustine   39, 270
Australopithecus   156ff.
authority of Scripture   104,
　　107f.
Ayala, F. J.   102n., 135n.

Baker, S.   94, 118f.
bara   80, 99f., 114, 122
Barclay, O. R.   130
Barnes, T. G.   57n.
Barton, J. M.   61
basement rocks   31f.

279

256; *see also* flood geology
attractiveness of 206ff.
interface with science 211ff., 245ff.
Creation Research Society 116
creation science *See* creationism
crossopterygii 152
crystallization 25, 31, 37, 51, 61
Cuffey, R. J. 95, 112
curse 127f., 168; *see also* fall, the
Cuvier, G. 212
cytology 97, 176ff., 195

Daniel 38, 40
Darnell, J. E. 196n.
Darwin, C. 11, 33, 87ff., 93, 96, 98, 106, 109, 112, 132, 143, 149, 155, 169, 186ff., 270
Darwinism 85, 111, 116f., 161ff., 191; *see also* evolution; neo-Darwinism; selection
Davidson, C. F. 59
Davies, J. D. 229n.
day, meaning of 81, 126, 135f., 186, 214, 224, 236f., 255, 265, 268
death 14, 93, 102, 105, 114, 168, 241, 263
decay constant *See* half-life
deception in natural world 37, 64f., 94, 216
deformation 51, 69
degeneration 241f.
deism 106
deposition rates 18, 28, 51ff., 70f.

descent with modification 169, 172
design *See* God's design
Devonian sediments 20f., 27
De Young, D. B. 50n.
dinosaurs 53, 81, 120, 172
divine intervention 77ff., 82, 142, 192, 242, 249; *see also* miracles
DNA sequences 135, 175, 179, 188
Dobzhansky, T. 86
dogs 111, 172f., 192
Doolittle, R. F. 195n.
Drosophila 86, 97, 173
Dubois, E. 158f.

Eden, Garden of 102
Eden, M. 143f.
Einstein, A. 124
Eldredge, N. 97n., 111
Elijah 247
Ellicott, C. J. 135f.
embryology 29, 89, 151
entropy *See* Thermodynamics
erosion 24, 33f., 51ff., 70, 72, 184
eukaryotes 176, 195f.
evaporites 21
Eve *See* Adam
evil 14
evolution:
  and endoctrination 110, 116
  and mechanism 165f., 169; *see also* mutation; selection
  and probability 132, 143f.; *see also* complexity of organs
  and thermodynamics 144ff., 168; *see also* Thermodynamics